END-PAPERS FROM THE BEANO BOOK 1958.

9 LITTLE, FURRY BEARS LEARNING HOW TO SKATE.
UMP!
ONE FELL LIKE A TON OF BRICKS —THEN THERE WERE 8.
REF
2
7
5
ONE SCORED AGAINST HIS SIDE — THEN THERE WERE 7.
6 LITTLE, FURRY BEARS TRY A SWALLOW DIVE.
ONE SWALLOWED HALF THE LAKE —THEN THERE WERE 5.

All through their 70 year history The Beano and The Dandy have been...

CRAZY ABOUT CREATURES!

JUMPING JIMINY THE KANGAROO WHO'S ALWAYS ON THE HOP. THE DANDY 1939-40.

CENTIPEDE PETE WITH THE HANDY FEET THE DANDY 1941.

KAT AND KANARY. THIS FUR AND FEATHER FEUD RAN IN THE BEANO 1952 – 56.

CONTENTS

This comic strip world is a perfect habitat for the most fantastic pets and bizarre birds and beasties. This book, the first in the 70 Years series, presents a super selection of our finest animal antics.

KORKY THE CAT

The comic world's top cat proved he really did have nine lives by staying on the front cover of The Dandy from 1937 until 1984. Even then it took someone as mighty as Desperate Dan to remove him.

Korky is a humanised cat, he can catch mice,catch a train, park his car and worries about the mortgage on his bungalow - a home he shares with a gang of very bold mice.

During the Second World War, 1939 – 45, Korky and The Dandy saw their part in the war effort as being to brighten up the lives of their millions of readers. Many of Korky's adventures were very patriotic, like the page below. Inspirational stuff in those dreadful dark times.

Favourite among the Korky strips are the tales involving his kitten nephews. Most Korky fans have a soft spot for the fun-loving little rogues.

Korky appeared in adverts encouraging readers to save waste paper. War-time children responded as the national paper shortage had caused The Dandy to be published once a fortnight.

SMARTY GRANDPA

(The Dandy 1937–40)

Early animal action from these Smarty Grandpa sets was beautifully drawn by Dudley D Watkins. Fans of The Broons strip in The Sunday Post will recognise the figure of Grandpa.

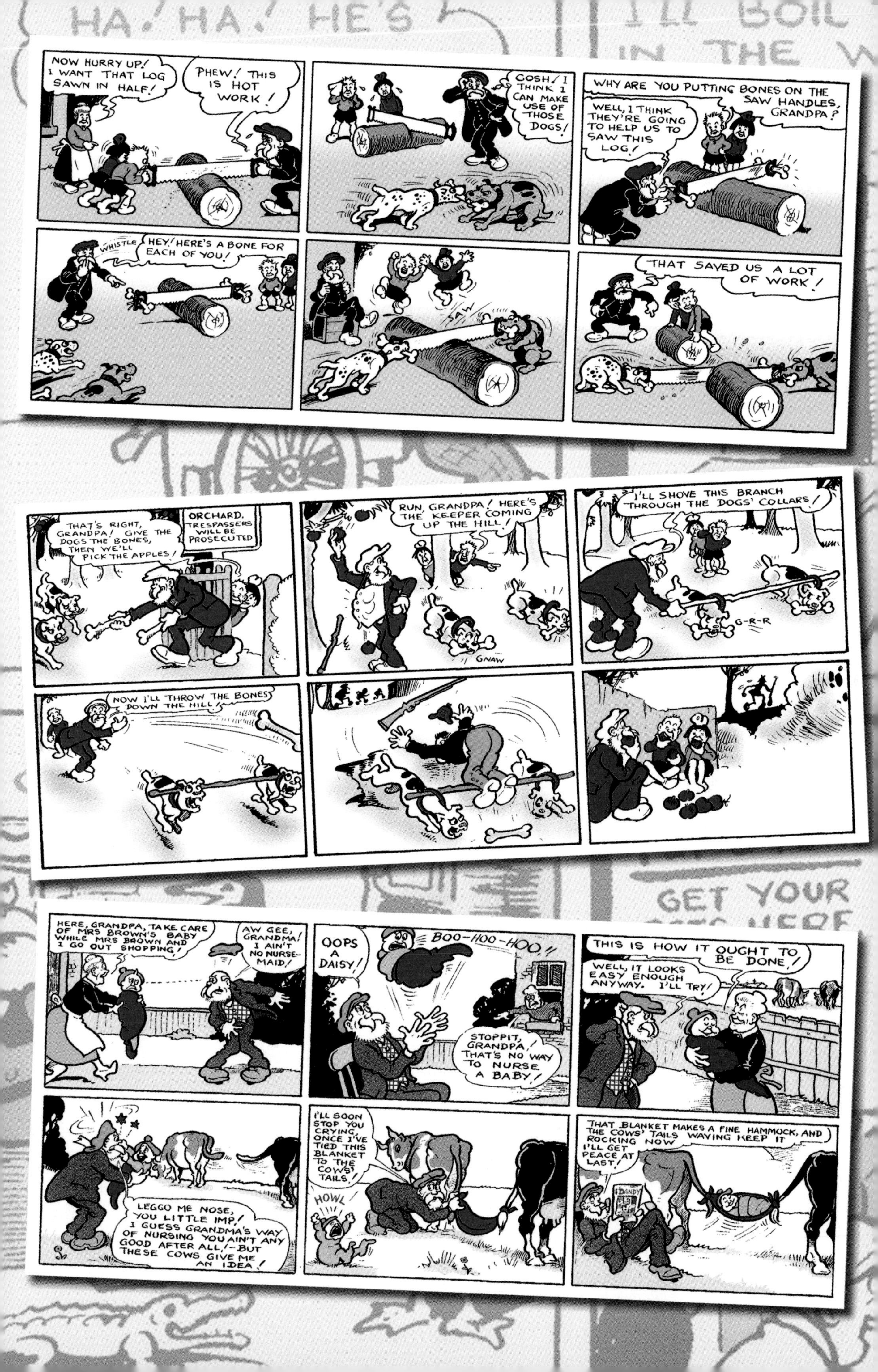

NOW HURRY UP! I WANT THAT LOG SAWN IN HALF!
PHEW! THIS IS HOT WORK!
GOSH! I THINK I CAN MAKE USE OF THOSE DOGS!
WHY ARE YOU PUTTING BONES ON THE SAW HANDLES, GRANDPA?
WELL, I THINK THEY'RE GOING TO HELP US TO SAW THIS LOG!
WHISTLE
HEY! HERE'S A BONE FOR EACH OF YOU!
SAW
THAT SAVED US A LOT OF WORK!
THAT'S RIGHT, GRANDPA! GIVE THE DOGS THE BONES, THEN WE'LL PICK THE APPLES!
ORCHARD. TRESPASSERS WILL BE PROSECUTED
RUN, GRANDPA! HERE'S THE KEEPER COMING UP THE HILL!
GNAW
I'LL SHOVE THIS BRANCH THROUGH THE DOGS' COLLARS!
G-R-R
NOW I'LL THROW THE BONES DOWN THE HILL!
HERE, GRANDPA, TAKE CARE OF MRS BROWN'S BABY WHILE MRS BROWN AND I GO OUT SHOPPING!
AW GEE, GRANDMA! I AIN'T NO NURSE-MAID!
OOPS A DAISY!
BOO-HOO-HOO!!
STOPPIT, GRANDPA! THAT'S NO WAY TO NURSE A BABY!
THIS IS HOW IT OUGHT TO BE DONE!
WELL, IT LOOKS EASY ENOUGH ANYWAY. I'LL TRY!
LEGGO ME NOSE, YOU LITTLE IMP! I GUESS GRANDMA'S WAY OF NURSING YOU AIN'T ANY GOOD AFTER ALL! — BUT THESE COWS GIVE ME AN IDEA!
I'LL SOON STOP YOU CRYING, ONCE I'VE TIED THIS BLANKET TO THE COWS' TAILS!
HOWL!
THAT BLANKET MAKES A FINE HAMMOCK, AND THE COWS' TAILS WAVING KEEP IT ROCKING NOW
I'LL GET PEACE AT LAST!
DANDY

HOT DAWG!

In July, 2001, a larger-than-life-sized, bronze, statue of Desperate Dan and his faithful Dawg was unveiled by schoolchildren in Dundee, Scotland.

Dan was a real desperado in his early years. A boxing bear tackles him in this rough-house strip from 1938.

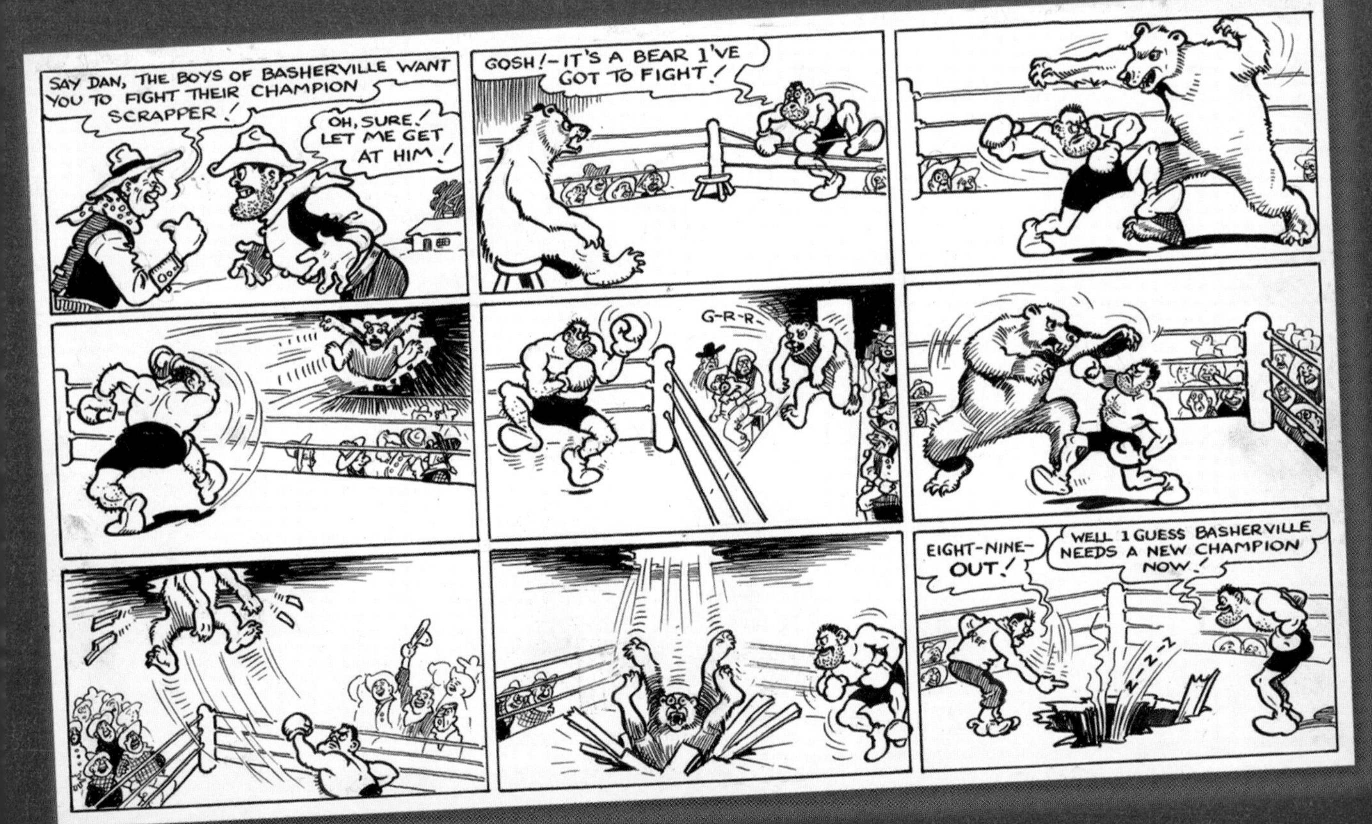

THE ORIGINAL FREDDY THE FLY FROM THE DANDY MONSTER COMIC 1951.

BIG EGGO

This colourful Ostrich cover showcased the quirky comic strips that The Beano became famous for. Although, this surreal,eat-anything bird would have laid an egg if he'd known The Beano he introduced would still be Britain's most popular comic 70 years on.

Eggo was originally billed as The Beano's Brainy Bird and the early storylines were about Eggo searching for his egg. In Beano No.8, Eggo mistakes a shiny bald head for his egg and receives a goldfish bowl full of water and fish over his own head in punishment. No sign of political correctness in those days. Eggo was always referred to as male so hopefully he did not actually lay the eggs himself...Hmm!

Soon,though, Big Eggo,like Korky the Cat before him, was moved by the scriptwriters to comic strip wonderland where oversized talking creatures lived and worked side by side with unquestioning humans.

REG CARTER
1886 – 1949

This artist drew the Big Eggo covers for all of its long run of 326 issues. He was primarily a postcard artist and a very accomplished one,having started drawing cards professionally at age 17. The two other characters he drew for The Beano were also creatures – Freddie Flipperfeet,the seal in 1947 and Peter Penguin in 1948.

In the strip above Eggo has a Barbers shop. Over the years he had great fun doing jobs such as Policeman, Zookeeper, Lumberjack, Postman and even a spell as the School Janitor.

Drawing the face of the enemy leader Adolf Hitler onto the horses landed the naughty beasts in trouble.

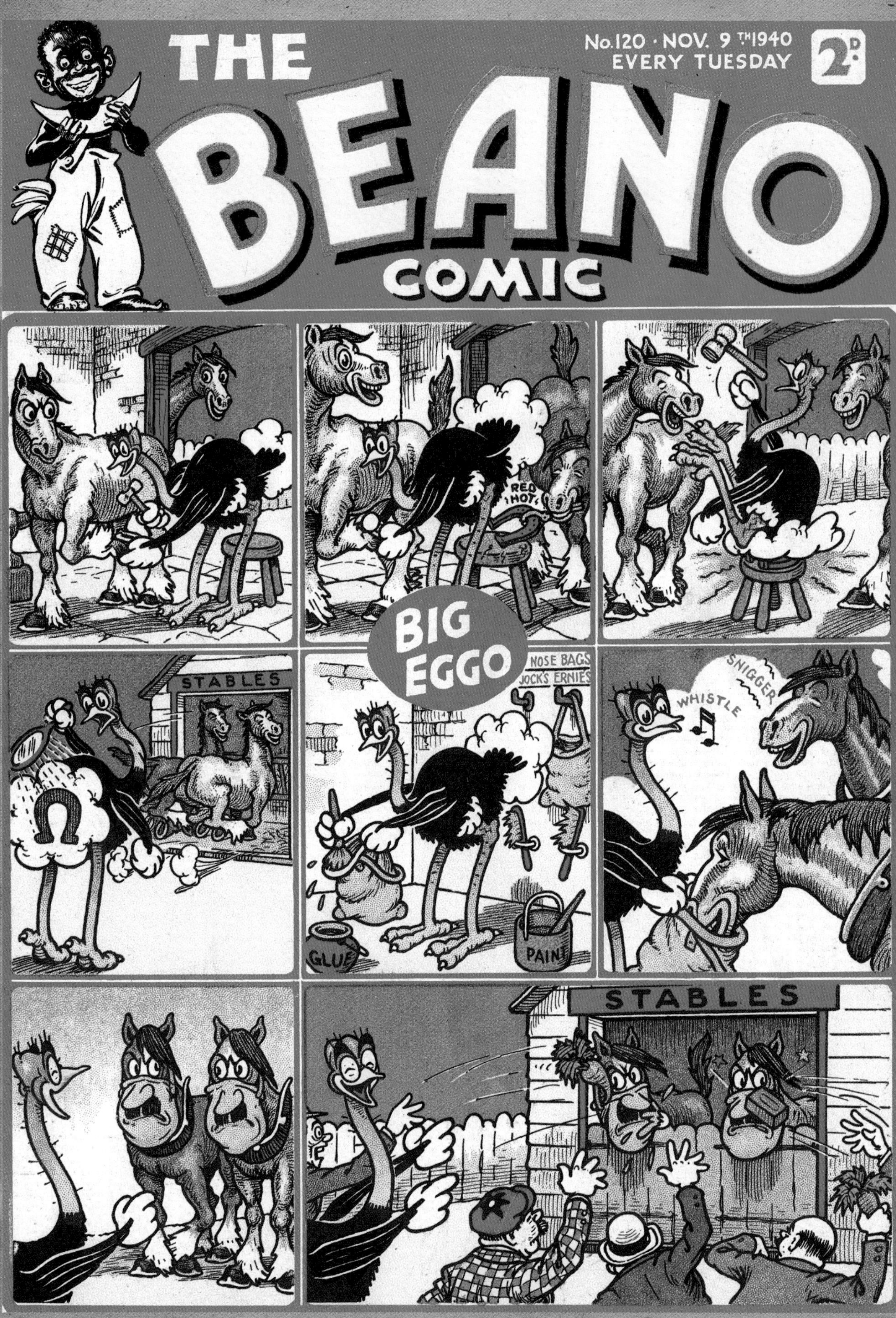

Is the chap throwing carrots really an enemy agent?

BIG EGGO'S WARTIME

Eggo did his bit for the war effort when he set about the enemy in a series of comic strip attacks.

I'LL DROP THIS EXPLOSIVE EGG ON HITLER'S PALACE.

THAT NIGHT OVER GERMANY

LOOK, GOERING, I'M SICK OF THIS — HALF A SAUSAGE BETWEEN US.

BIG EGGO

MY PATIENCE IS EXHAUSTED! BRING ME AN EGG!

NOW, WHERE SHALL I PUT IT ?

HI! I'LL TAKE THAT FINE BIG EGG FOR ADOLF'S BREAKFAST!

ACH! WHAT A FINE BIG EGG! AT LAST I VILL HAF DER GOOT BREAKFAST!

TAP TAP

BANG!

TA TA!

But Eggo meets the Terriers firing.
A new idea, they're inspiring.

I'LL MAKE A HEAP OF THESE STONES

A heap of stones the bird collects.
I wonder what Eggo expects.

The monkeys cannot see the fun
As targets for his patent "gun."

BIG EGGO'S NEPHEWS

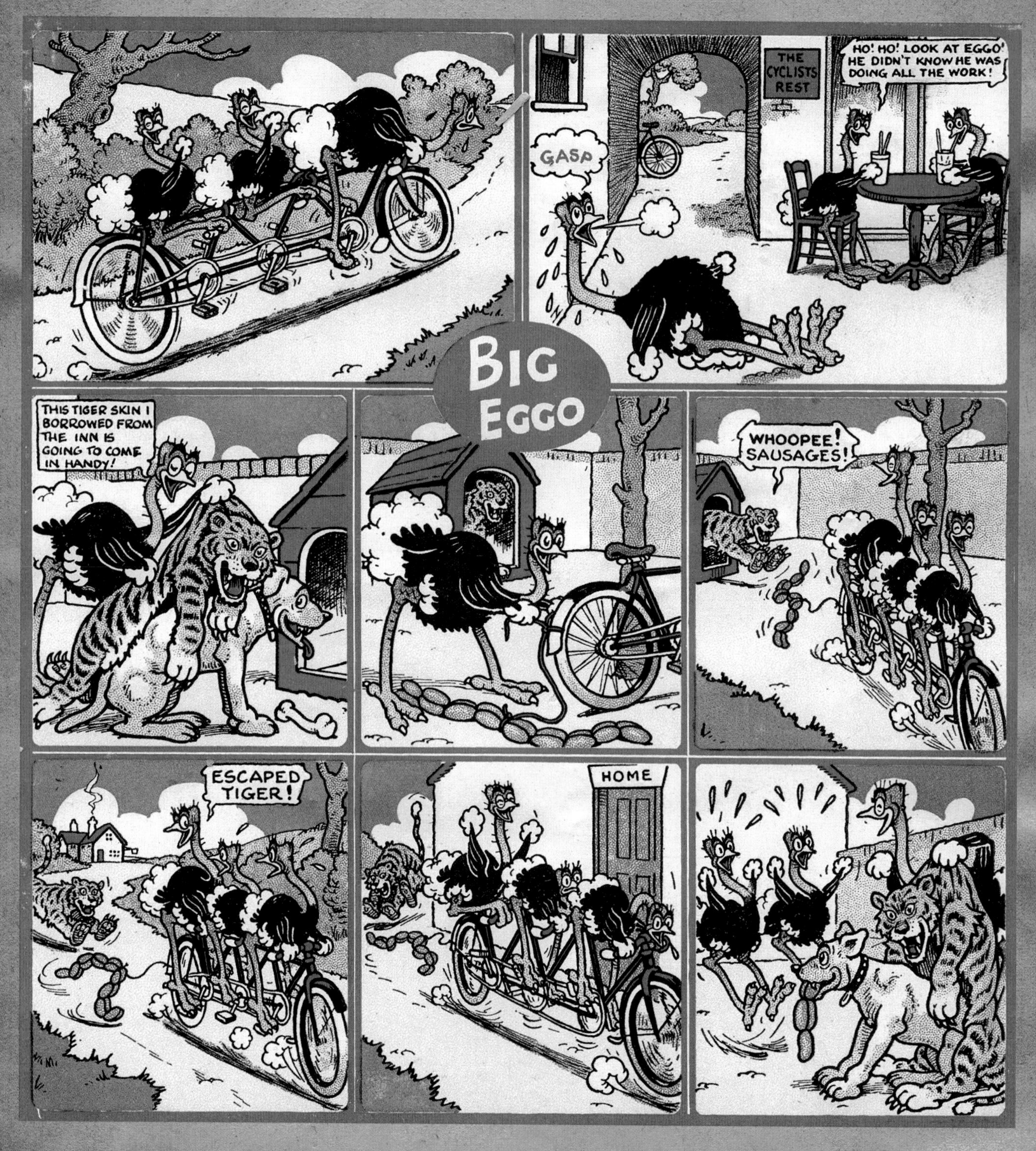

The Beano No.327. Eggo has a black and white strip inside the comic.

Mirroring Korky the cat again, Big Eggo often landed with looking after his nephews. Some of the funniest storylines involved this threesome.

CLASSIC PANSY POTTER FROM THE BEANO BOOK 1940.
PANSY POTTER
THE STRONG MAN'S DAUGHTER
HOW DO YOU LIKE WATER SQUIRTED ON YOU, PANSY?
HEY YOU! WHAT ARE YOU ---- GURGLE!
SWOOSH
DUST BIN
WE'LL BE GOIN' NOW - S'LONG!
ALL RIGHT, YOU NASTY BOYS I'LL GET YOU FOR THAT!
I'VE GOT AN IDEA!
HUH, I'LL SHOW THOSE LADS WHAT'S WHAT IN A MINUTE!
ZOO NOW OPEN

"Wat-er cheek!" said Pansy when the boys washed her face with their squirt.

Who let the dogs out? His Lordship in The Beano January 1939.

RED RORY
OF THE EAGLES
Adventure picture stories were very popular in both comics. June 1952 saw the arrival in The Beano of a new action character, red-haired Rory McPherson and his trained Golden Eagles, Flame and Fury. Most of the Red Rory stories were illustrated by Paddy Brennan. But this episode from The Beano Book 1959 was drawn by Andy Hutton.

1. It was the year 1746, after the Battle of Culloden. Prince Charlie's army had been scattered to the hills and glens where they were hunted as outlaws by the Redcoats. In a small, isolated valley in the Highlands, a lone Redcoat was fording a stream on his horse. The sky was dark and thunder rolled around the hills. Suddenly a jagged streak of lightning flashed into the river bank. The glare of the lightning and the crackle of the thunder frightened the horse, which reared up, throwing its rider heavily into the foaming river. Up on the rugged hillside a sturdy, red-haired boy clad in a rough shirt and kilt witnessed the incident. He was Red Rory, the boy outlaw and he had been closely following the Redcoat soldier's movements. Beside Rory hovered his trained eagles Flame and Fury

2. The Redcoat was wearing thigh-length boots which immediately filled with water. He had great difficulty in keeping his head above water as he threshed violently with his arms to save himself from drowning. The terrified horse splashed across the river and disappeared as Rory ran down to the river's edge.

3. Rory plunged into the river and struck out strongly towards the Redcoat. The man was exhausted and in danger of being swept under by the strong current. His weight was too much for Rory to support alone, but with the eagles gripping the man's cross-straps, the Redcoat was soon pulled to safety.

4. The soldier lay on the bank recovering his strength. When at last he felt well enough to move, Rory decided to take the man to one of his secret hideouts. With the Redcoat leaning heavily on him, Rory made slow progress, but at last the pair reached Rory's cave in the hills.

5. The cave was warm and dry and before long the Redcoat had recovered sufficiently to explain to Rory the mission that had brought him to the lonely glen. He was a courier on his way to a nearby Redcoat camp, bearing a pardon from the King for all outlaw Highlanders in the area

6. Rory took the pardon from the Redcoat and read it eagerly. A few days before, some of his friends had been taken prisoner by the Redcoats and were under sentence of death. The execution was due to take place that very day. Suddenly, with wildly flapping wings, the eagles flew out of the cave. Rory was puzzled by their strange behaviour.

7. The eagles had sensed danger. As they disappeared from the cave, a jagged streak of lightning struck the hillside above the cave, dazzling Rory and the Redcoat. There was a tremendous crash and then huge boulders and tons of rubble crashed down. When the landslide ended, the pair saw that the entrance to the cave was blocked.

8. Rory and the Redcoat were trapped in the cave until help came. If the pardon was not delivered that day, it would be too late to save Rory's friends. At once Rory sat down to scrawl a message on a scrap of parchment the Redcoat produced from his pouch.

9. Then Rory began to tackle the earth and stones that blocked the cave entrance. With gloved hands he tore at the rubble, throwing it aside. Rory knew that he could never hope to clear it all. At last, he made a hole big enough to get his hand through.

10. Tying the message round a stone, Rory squeezed his hand through the opening. A shrill whistle brought Fury gliding down. Rory shouted instructions to the eagle and tossed out the message which was deftly caught in Fury's strong talons. Then the great bird flew quickly away over the hills.

11. At top speed, the eagle flew towards the hideout of some of Rory's friends. The bird wheeled overhead, screaming harshly. When the clansmen came running out of the came to investigate, the eagle dropped amongst them the message tied around the stone. It was picked up and read.

12. With Fury showing the way, the Highlanders set out over the wild countryside. They reached the cave and at once they set to work to clear the entrance. It was hard going, but after an hour or so, the boulders were removed from the entrance. Rory and the Redcoats were released. Quickly Rory gave an account of what had happened.

13. The Redcoat was suffering from shock and in no condition to continue on his way. The Highlanders agreed to take him to their cave. Lachlan, a sturdy Highlander, carried him there, while Rory took charge of the pardon. Time was precious now. The boy decided to deliver the pardon himself to the Redcoats' barracks. But how was he to get there?

14. The redcoat was comfortable in the cave and Rory knew that he would be well cared for by the Highlanders. With a shrill whistle Rory summoned his eagles. He had a special task for them to do. Somewhere in the area the Redcoat's horse was to be found and Rory needed it.

15. The great birds disappeared over the hills and valleys in search of the horse. They found it grazing quickly in a valley, completely recovered from its fright at the river. The eagles wheeled overhead, watching it closely. Then the great birds swooped down on the animal.

16. Before the horse could bolt, Fury caught hold of the reins in its talons. The startled horse reared in fright. Then, finding it could not break free, it broke into a wild gallop. The eagles began to force it in the direction they wanted it to go. At last they brought it to the cave.

17. Rory leapt into the saddle and seized the reins. "Well done, Flame and Fury!" he called out, as he urged the horse into a gallop and set off on the long, dangerous ride to the barracks. With great skill, Rory kept the horse on its feet as he rode down the rugged mountainside.

18. Rory reached the barracks with no time to spare. The condemned Highlanders were lined up for execution and the Redcoats had their rifles at the ready. Rory galloped on to the square, waving the pardon above his head. The officer in charge signalled to the soldiers to lower their rifles. When he had read the pardon, the officer ordered the Highlanders' release.

19. The Highlanders were overjoyed at their narrow, last-minute escape from death. Cheering wildly they lifted Rory shoulder high and with a piper leading the way, the boy was carried in triumph back to Lachlan's cave in the hills. The Highlanders owed their lives to Rory and for that they would always be grateful to him – and to his golden eagles.

BLACK BOB

THE DANDY WONDER DOG!

One man and his dogs

Black Bob made his debut in the Dandy in November 1944 in the first of a long series of text stories featuring the exploits of this canine superhero. Black Bob's appearance coincided with the cinematic success of another famous dog, Lassie, whose first film, Lassie Come Home had been released a year earlier. The illustrations for the text stories, and the later picture stories, were all from the hand of Jack Prout, a D.C.Thomson staff artist. Jack's style brought the tales of Andrew Glenn and his canine companion to life and shortly before he retired, it is rumoured that the Dandy staff gave Jack a dog that bore a remarkable likeness to the character he had drawn for over 20 years.

This Black Bob from 9.10.55 was the last ever Dandy text story.

There are dozens of evil men in the circus—And they're all after Black Bob!

BLACK BOB

An Uneven Fight.

A STRUGGLE was taking place in a deep ditch at the rear of the circus ground on the edge of Galashiels. Black Bob was locked in a desperate fight with the India-Rubber Man from the circus, a short thickset fellow who shouted for help as he struggled.

Andrew Glenn and his cousin Tom came running up to the spot where the struggle was taking place. They had been lying in wait for this man to prevent him reaching the circus, for he had in his possession a very important letter belonging to Tom Glenn.

Behind them there were loud shouts from the Circus Americano as several of the circus men came running towards the spot to see what was wrong with the India-Rubber Man.

These men from the Circus Americano were at the root of all the trouble which Andrew and Tom Glenn had been having.

Their boss, Don Danli, was an evil rogue. He had found out that Tom Glenn possessed a chart showing where Captain Kidd, the famous pirate, had hidden a fabulous treasure and he was sparing no effort to lay hands on this chart. But Black Bob and the Glenn cousins were fighting back.

Their idea was to fight against Danli until Tom received word from his lawyers in London, who were trying to arrange with the Honduras Government for Tom to remove the treasure.

But just after Tom had received the letter, his pocket had been picked by one of the circus men. Now the two cousins and Black Bob were trying to stop the pick-pocket's companion from reaching the circus and handing Tom's letter over to Don Danli.

But Black Bob had never found it so difficult to hold anyone before. As fast as he gripped his opponent, the India-Rubber Man twisted in some extraordinary way and was free again. He held a thick stick and with this he kept trying to strike the sheepdog.

Andrew Glenn was the first to arrive, and as he looked down at the tussling pair he saw Bob grab one of the man's hands between his teeth. But the India-Rubber Man had been well named, for his skin was loose and rubbery—he slid his hand out of Bob's grasp.

Andrew Glenn waited his opportunity and jumped on top of the India-Rubber Man, crooking an arm round the circus man's neck and thus holding him in a stranglehold.

"The registered letter—where is it?" Glenn demanded.

Any other man would have been forced to give up under such a hold but the India-Rubber Man twisted himself right round so that he was facing Andrew Glenn, and drove his knee into the shepherd's stomach. At the same time he gave a yell, for Bob had seized him by the ankle.

The shepherd hung on as the man squirmed. He hoped Tom would go through the man's pockets, but Tom Glenn was already turning to face the first three circus men who had scrambled through the hedge. Don Danli was one of them, and he was red with rage.

"Settle them once and for all!" he was shouting. "There's nobody about to see what we do."

Tom used only his clenched fists, whereas Danli's two companions had clubs, and others were hurrying towards the fight.

Black Bob now had a proper grip on the India-Rubber Man and pulled his legs from under him. The man went down with Glenn on top of him, and as the circus man's breath was knocked from his body, the shepherd dived a hand into the man's nearest pocket.

Glenn was lucky. His fingers found the registered letter belonging to his cousin. He snatched it and stuffed it into his own pocket.

He scrambled out of the ditch, and saw Tom reeling under the blows of the two circus hands, while Don Danli ran towards the ditch, a knife in his hand. The shepherd crouched and waited for the attack, but Black Bob did not hesitate. He dived past his master and sprang at the raised knife hand.

Don Danli snarled and struck down at the dog, but Bob met the down-coming wrist and gripped with his sharp teeth. Danli screamed and dropped the knife, beating at Bob with his other fist to make him let go.

Andrew Glenn now had the thick stick which the India-Rubber Man had been wielding, and he saw his chance to run in and swing it at the South American's head. Down went Don Danli, and the shepherd raced to his cousin's aid.

Tom had been beaten to his knees by blows from his attackers' clubs just as Andrew Glenn arrived. Glenn lashed about so savagely with the stick that he drove the circus men back long enough for Tom to get to his feet.

"I've got it!" Gasped Andrew, grabbing his cousin by the arm. "Let's make for the main road and find the police. Hi, Bob!"

They ran for the road, but more of Danli's men came running up to block their path.

Andrew Glenn saw that they could not reach the lane and he swerved away from Danli's men, bursting through a gap in the hedge and into the field which was the circus ground. It was the only way open to them.

Behind, the pursuers turned back to help Don Danli to his feet. The circus owner was still shouting for the two cousins to be stopped, for by now he knew about the registered letter they had and he guessed its importance.

Panic In The Circus.

IT happened that most of the other circus men were at the far end of the ground, putting up a large canvas screen which had blown down during the night. They did not hear the shouts from the field, so the two cousins and Bob were able to make their way, unseen, as far as the big circus tent.

From inside came the crack of a whip, and the harsh voice of a man. Through an open flap Andrew Glenn saw the ringmaster rehearsing the troupe of trained horses.

Andrew Glenn glanced over his shoulder. Danli and his men would soon be in sight again, and there were an unknown number of men in front of them. The three would stand little chance of escape unless they did something to take attention away from themselves.

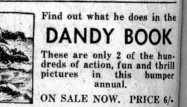

He stopped, grabbed Black Bob, and pointed through the flap of the big tent. "Scatter them, Bob!" he hissed, and gave a signal which Black Bob understood. He darted through the opening into the tent

Bob reappeared in picture story form the following year.

Why is a sailor never a sailor? — Because he's either ashore or aboard.

and burst into the ring, barking loudly.

Snarling and barking, Bob snapped at the horses until he had scattered them in all directions. In vain did the ringmaster shout and crack his whip. The horses were highly-strung animals and were frightened by this black and white fury which had burst into their midst. They jumped out of the ring and made for the nearest exit.

Within a minute the ten horses were charging all over the circus ground, spreading great confusion.

Andrew Glenn whistled for Bob, who came back with lolling tongue, as though he had enjoyed this bit of fun.

"We ought to be able to sneak out during all this uproar," he told his cousin. "The great thing is to keep out of sight, and—Too late! we've been seen!"

Don Danli and his men had burst through the hedge and had caught sight of the three fugitives.

It was bad luck being seen, and there was nothing for it but to run again. Then their luck changed. One of the frantic horses collided with a rope which was steadying a cage where monkeys were kept. The jerk pulled the cage over with a crash, the door flew open, and a dozen monkeys escaped.

Screeching and chattering, they scattered. Some leaped on to the backs of passing horses. Others pelted the circus men with anything they could seize.

The monkeys and the horses were valuable, and some of the men thought it was more important to round them up than to stop the two Scotsmen and their dog, so Bob and his companions were able to slip through the cordon that was closing round them, and to reach the canvas screen which had been erected near the main road.

It had been put up to prevent people from looking into the menagerie section of the circus without paying for admission and it was not much of a barrier. When Andrew and his cousin grabbed one of the stakes and pulled, they soon had it down. A moment later they had jumped over the fallen screen into the ditch which bordered the road.

Behind them they heard Don Danli roar: "Stop them! Ten pounds to the man who can stop them!"

Tom was staggering, for he had suffered many hard blows, but they had run only a few yards before a car came round the corner, going towards the town.

"Andrew Glenn!" shouted the driver, and pulled up.

It was a Selkirk farmer who knew the shepherd and Black Bob well.

"Give us a lift into the town!" gasped Glenn. "The circus men are after us."

The farmer asked no questions, but opened one of the doors, and they all piled in. Just as the first of the circus men reached the road the car sped off down the road to Galashiels.

"Now what's it all about?" asked the farmer. "How'd ye get into a tangle with those foreigners, and who's this with ye, Glenn—a brother?"

"It's my cousin," said Andrew Glenn, as he watched Tom tear open the registered letter and read the contents.

A moment later Tom looked up.

"Could you drive me to the police station?" he asked. "There's no longer any reason why we should keep this to ourselves, Andrew."

"Then you've got the news you've waited for in that letter?" asked Bob's master.

"Yes, I've got what I hoped for," replied his cousin. "Now we can tell the police about Don Danli and his bunch!"

Don Danli's Flight.

VERY soon Tom Glenn was pouring out his story about Captain Kidd's treasure to a sergeant at the police station.

"Then the circus is all a fake?" he asked.

"It's a real circus, but it belongs to Don Danli, and he's been using it as a cover while he searched for me," replied Tom. "He's got those men completely under his thumb, and makes them do whatever he wishes."

The sergeant phoned for the inspector and the two cousins talked in a corner while they waited for him.

"This letter is from my lawyers in London. They've received a message from the Honduras Embassy saying that the government are willing to allow me a half share of any treasure that I may find. Now we've only got to deal with Don Danli," Tom said, and his eyes sparkled with excitement.

Within half an hour police from Galashiels, Selkirk, and Melrose were all arriving at the circus ground.

Black Bob, his master, and Tom Glenn went, too. Seeing that the police were in force, the circus men stared sullenly and let them march up to Don Danli's caravan.

Don Danli was not to be found, and it was ten minutes before someone admitted that he had left in the circus helicopter.

Word was immediately phoned around the countryside for watch to be kept for the helicopter, but up to the time when Tom Glenn had picked out all those circus men who had been helping Don Danli, no word of the escaped circus boss had been received.

Half a dozen of the circus employees were taken to the police station, and a police guard was put over the others. As Andrew Glenn was anxious about his flock the police sergeant agreed to drive him back to the glen with Black Bob, leaving Tom to settle everything with the police in Galashiels.

The glen looked as peaceful as ever when they left the police car and climbed the hillside towards the grazing grounds.

Suddenly, however, Black Bob stopped and began to sniff the breeze, growling. Then with a mighty bound he went up a steep bank and over the top. A few moments later the shepherd heard him barking furiously.

Andrew Glenn scrambled up the bank, and then he saw the reason for Bob's excitement. About a hundred yards away lay a smashed helicopter. It had crashed in a patch of thick gorse bushes. Black Bob had reached the spot and was tugging at something among the wreckage. There was a strong smell of petrol in the air. It was this that had attracted Bob's attention.

His master was soon on the spot, and he saw that what Black Bob was trying to pull clear was the still form of Don Danli.

Andrew Glenn dragged the South American out and found that he was still alive, though unconscious. In his desperation to escape from the police Danli had tried to pilot the helicopter himself, but he hadn't known enough about flying.

Moments later Black Bob carried a message for his master down to the village, asking the postmaster to telephone for the police.

The police were soon on the scene, and once the dazed Don Danli was handed over to their care, Bob and Andrew Glenn were able to round up their sheep and go home.

Tom Glenn returned to the cottage some hours later in a hired car, to announce that he would be leaving the following day for Glasgow, to catch a ship to South America.

"But for you, Andrew, and for Black Bob, I wouldn't be having this chance of seeking the treasure of Captain Kidd," he said. "Would you like to come with me and share my part of the treasure?"

Andrew Glenn fondled Bob's silky ears as he looked out of the window.

"No, Tom. Thanks all the same, but Bob and I belong here. We've got all the treasure that we need—good health, a good home, plenty of interesting work, and good friends. We want no part of Captain Kidd's treasure, Tom, but one day come back and tell us all about it. We'll try to give you a peaceful holiday next time!"

When the Falklands conflict blew up between Britain and Argentina in 1982 the Black Bob story running at the time concerned our canine hero's kidnap in Argentina. The then editor received a great number of letters from readers concerned about Black Bob's safety in a country with whom we were at war.

March 14, 1982

Dear Editor,

I am becoming increasingly concerned about the safety of Black Bob. Not only has he been kidnapped, but is on the loose in Argentina, a country with whom we are at war.

I sincerely hope you have made representations to the government about this situation and will endeavour to assure the safety of this poor, unfortunate animal.

Yours hopefully,

Emily.

EVEN THE SURLY OLD RAM WAS WARY OF HIM.
BOB'S MASTER TAUGHT HIM TRICKS LIKE THIS ONE — SEEKING AND FETCHING THINGS.
BUT HERE'S AN ESCAPE-TRICK HE LEARNED HIMSELF!
FOR BOB LIKED FREEDOM, AND PLENTY OF FUN.
HE WAS TAUGHT TO DRIVE DUCKS, AND SO LEARNED THE WAY TO DRIVE SHEEP.
HE WAS TIRELESS. HE RESCUED A SCHOOLBOY'S CAP FROM A FAST-RUNNING RIVER
ON THE VERY DAY WHEN HE WON HIS FIRST SHEEPDOG CHAMPION'S CUP
BLACK BOB
AND THAT IS THE STORY OF HOW BLACK BOB GREW UP.
1950
1953
BOB
1957
1961

Shown here are the back covers of some of the Black Bob books. This is the easiest way to date these books which have similar covers.

The Black Bob picture stories appeared in newspapers as well as the Dandy.

ANDREW GLENN, the Selkirk shepherd, was spending a ten day holiday with his friend, Tom Laird, who had settled down on a croft on Birsay Island. And ten exciting, pellmell days they turned out to be. One day the two men were fishing in the bay. Black Bob, of course, was with them, and it was his keen ears that first picked up the sound of a motor-boat engine far across the bay. Bob barked and sprang to the bow of the little coble.

2—" Strangers, surely," remarked Glenn as he pointed to the motor-boat. " Aye, and headin' for the shore," answered Tom Laird, as he reeled in the lines. " We'd better get back, Andrew, and see who they are and what they want." Without a word the shepherd grabbed the oars and pulled for the beach. Laird had told him of rumours of men who were making raids on lonely islands to steal sheep. Strangers could mean trouble.

3—When they landed Glenn turned to Laird. " You go to the croft and join Mrs Laird and Peggy," he said. " Bob and I will see what these men are up to." The shepherd headed inland with Bob at his heels, and from a hilltop he saw the strangers. Two roughly-dressed, tough-looking men they were, and they were stealing sheep ! So the rumour about the sheep-lifters was true—and here they were on Birsay, taking some of Tom Laird's.

4—" Come on, Bob," said Glenn. " We must put a stop to this game." Off he raced behind the collie. These sheep, Glenn knew, were prize animals. That was the reason for the visit by the motor-boat raiders. The sheep would fetch a big price. As Glenn ran down he was seen by the thieves, who hurriedly drove the sheep over a plank bridge across a ravine. Then one of them turned and hurled the bridge into the depths, so that no one could follow.

5—It was a cunning trick, for the gap was too wide for Glenn to jump. By the time he got across they would be aboard their boat and out to sea. But the sheep-stealers forgot about Black Bob, who raced ahead of his master to tackle the crooks on his own. The big-hearted collie reached the edge of the chasm and took off in a daring leap. Glenn held his breath. It seemed an impossible jump even for Black Bob. Would he succeed?

6—" Good boy," said the shepherd as Bob landed on the opposite side and scrambled to safety. " Go on, Bob ! Harry them !" Glenn began to clamber down the rocky side of the ravine, in a hurry to join his dog in the fight against the robbers. The men had a dog with them, a spotted mongrel, but it didn't seem too keen to fight. Black Bob raced round about the men, barking. They pelted him with stones, but dodging these was easy work for Bob.

7—By this time the men were only a few yards from their boat. In two minutes they would be able to put the sheep aboard and run for it. But Bob was too quick for them. First he tackled the mongrel, and after a short scuffle the cowardly brute ran away, yelping, with a clipped ear. Then the collie turned his attention to the stolen sheep, driving them back towards the ravine. All the while he kept dodging the stones thrown at him.

8—The two scoundrels were furious at being baulked. They came dashing after Bob, urging the faint-hearted mongrel to attack. It tried, but at a snap from Bob it veered off, squealing. The collie kept the three sheep moving, and still dodged every stone hurled by the crooks. Then, as the men neared the ravine, Andrew Glenn came clambering up over the side. The sheep-stealers stopped, wondering what to do. The shepherd barred their way.

Two toughs who weren't tough enough

ANDREW GLENN threw down his cap and rolled his sleeves up even higher. "Come on, I'm ready!" he shouted. He couldn't retreat, because the ravine was behind him. He had to make a fight of it. The two men were wary. They could see Glenn was a big strong man. But still, they were two to one, and they knew all the rough-house tricks. "Get that yokel out of the way, Basher!" yelled the man wearing a hat.

2—The first roughneck ran at Glenn, swinging his fists. Then he fell, knocked senseless by a blow with all Glenn's strength behind it. Jake Briggs, as the other man was called, rushed in with his stick upraised, but a sharp bark from Black Bob put the shepherd on his guard. He swung round and smashed his fist into the man's face. At the same time Bob leaped up and fixed his teeth in Jake's arm, hanging on for all he was worth.

3—Frantically Jake tried to shake Bob off, but Bob wouldn't let go. Then Glenn lashed out again and Jake crumpled up. The shepherd wasted no time. While the sheep-stealers were still senseless he stripped off their belts and ties and used these to truss them hand and foot. Bob stood guard over Basher while Glenn bound Briggs, and in a short time both were well and truly tied so that they couldn't break loose. They were recovering now.

4—Glenn set off to get Tom Laird, leaving Black Bob to guard Jake and Basher. "Watch them, Bob," he ordered, and set off for Corbie Croft. It took him quite a while, for he had to climb down and then up the ravine. He told Tom Laird what had happened, and the two of them took ropes with them and went back. The bridge was replaced after some trouble, and then, with their legs freed, the two crooks were forced to walk to the croft.

5—Briggs and Basher were sullen and scared, and in silence they trudged over the hill to the little croft. Glenn and Laird decided to take no chances. They put the prisoners into the stable and locked it. The shepherd had a look round the outside, and then, satisfied, he said:—"That'll hold them for the night, Tom. Bob will give the alarm if they try to break out. To-morrow I'll take them over to the police station on Orisay Island."

6—Next morning early Glenn and Laird hauled their prisoners out of the stable and marched them down to the motor-boat. The men were in an ugly mood, desperate at the thought of being handed over to the police. Basher struggled to get away from Glenn, but the shepherd's firm grip on his coat collar soon forced the bruiser aboard the boat. Tom Laird had plenty of work to do on his croft, so Glenn went in the boat with Bob as escort.

7—Once the prisoners were on board the motor-boat, Laird tied his rowing boat on tow behind it. "You'll need this, Andrew," he said. "The police will probably keep their motor-boat, so you'll have to row back." The two sheep-stealers sat in the stern, cursing their luck, while Bob watched them. Glenn steered. He waved to Laird as he started the engine and set off on the four-mile journey to Orisay to hand the men over to the police.

8—The boat was fast and they made good progress at first, but Glenn suddenly heard a scared shout from one of the prisoners. "Hi! The boat's sprung a leak!" yelled Basher. "We're sinking!" Glenn saw the water spouting in through the floorboards. Something had to be done, and quickly. Yet if he released the sheep-stealers they were sure to attack him. The men kept bawling at him to do something, and the bubbling water kept rising.

THE boat was half full of water now, liable to sink any minute. " I'll have to take a chance," Glenn decided. He stopped the engine and the boat at once began to settle at alarming speed. " Come here, you two—quick !" he ordered. The two toughs scrambled over the seats towards him and Glenn untied the hands of his prisoners. " Get busy baling," he cried. " It's our only chance." The water was already up to their knees and rising fast.

2—There was a bucket and a couple of tins under the thwarts. Glenn's idea was to force the men to help him bale out the water, and so keep the boat afloat. But those two had no intention of helping. As soon as both were free they cast off the tow-rope and jumped into the water before Glenn could stop them. They swam for the rowing boat, scrambled aboard and got out the oars, leaving Bob and his master stranded in the sinking motor-boat.

3—" Serves ye right !" bawled Briggs, as Basher rowed the boat away. " I hope ye drown—you and that dog !" Glenn was silent, but under his breath he was blaming himself for a fool. " I might have known," he told himself. But at once he got to work. His only chance was to bale the water out faster than it came in. He seized the bucket and worked like a madman. The water swirled at knee-depth, bubbling up from the hole in the bottom.

4—After several minutes of hard effort Glenn saw he had gained just a little on the incoming water. The island of Orisay was still more than a mile away. He wondered how he could reach it, and then an idea struck him. Luckily the water hadn't reached the engine yet, so Glenn set it going. Next he turned the wheel till the boat's nose pointed at the island. " Here, Bob. Take hold," he said, and set the clever dog to steady the wheel with his paws.

5—It was a slim chance. Glenn couldn't both bale and steer, but he trusted Black Bob to keep the wheel steady while he kept on baling, and the boat was set for a straight run into the harbour. Glenn grabbed the bucket again and baled for dear life. It was back-breaking work, but the shepherd kept at it, and every minute brought them nearer to Orisay. " We'll make it yet !" Glenn gasped, snatching a moment to see how far they had to go.

6—By the time the motor-boat limped into the harbour it was well down in the water, and Glenn was very tired. But two fishermen had seen that the boat was in trouble, and they threw the shepherd a rope. Glenn pulled the craft alongside the quay, and there, within a few minutes, it sank. " Just made it, eh, Bob?" said Glenn. He thanked the fishermen for their help, and then turned to the police sergeant who came hurrying down to the harbour.

7—The sergeant was a man of action, and he proved it as soon as he heard Glenn's story. " They can't have got far in a rowing boat," he said. " We'll nab them ! Dougal, we'll use your boat." Dougal, one of the fishermen, immediately got his engine started and they put out to sea. In ten minutes they sighted Laird's boat with the two sheep-stealers. What a shock it was for those rogues to see Glenn as the fishing vessel came alongside.

8—The rascals were overpowered and handcuffed, and it wasn't long till they were in a cell at Orisay police station. " A good job of work, Mr Glenn," said the local inspector when the men were put away. " You deserve a reward." The shepherd laughed. " If there is a reward," he said, " make it a nice plate of juicy bones and send it to Bob here. He earned it." However, both he and Bob got a good meal before they started back to Birsay.

A cart for Peggy—a harness for Bob

GLENN was up early next day, in spite of the fact that he had stayed up late the night before, telling the Lairds all about his adventure with the two sheep-stealers. Laird had been busy during the past few months. The land had been broken up and crops sown. The hay had been cut, but it still had to be taken in and stacked near the croft. Black Bob acted in his old job of guardian to little Peggy, and she was " helping," too.

2—All day they toiled at the haymaking. Peggy was a happy little girl, and she prattled away to Bob as she raked wisps of hay together. " You're a big help, Peggy," said Andrew Glenn as he forked her little bundle of hay on to the farmcart. " Off we go !" He was about to lift her on to the broad back of the horse and walk alongside to the stackyard when Peggy had a sudden thought. " Me want a wee cart," she lisped, pointing at the load of hay.

3—Glenn smiled. " Good idea, Peggy," he said, patting her head. " I'll make one for you. But what about a horse?" The wee lass turned and clutched one of Black Bob's silky ears. " Bob's my horse," she cried. And the collie barked as if he understood what all the talk was about. So after the hay was brought in Andrew Glenn got busy making a cart for Peggy, and Bob and she watched him at work. The collie was as interested as the girl.

4—A few pieces of wood nailed together formed the body of the cart, and two old pram-wheels were discovered lying in the stables. " I'll soon have it ready," said Glenn, when Peggy brought her mother down to see her new cart. " But we'll need harness for Bob." That was Mrs Laird's job. She got her husband to cut up some old leather harness into small pieces, and then she stitched them into a set of harness to fit around Bob.

5—When the job was done, and Bob was harnessed in the shafts of the little cart, Peggy was lifted aboard. She was delighted and grasped the reins in the proper way, just as she had seen her father do. " Gee up !" she commanded, and Black Bob strode off as proud as Punch, carrying his little passenger around the croft and turning to her tug on the reins in great style. Glenn and the Lairds looked on as Peggy drove Bob up and down.

6—It was a merry time for the little family on Birsay. But trouble was near at hand again. Suddenly Glenn gave a shout. " Fire !" he yelled. " Look ! In the haystack !" Right enough, there was smoke coming from a spot near the foot of one of the stacks. Hurriedly the men filled pails with water from the horse trough and dashed to the stacks. The fire by now had a strong hold of one haystack. Somehow they must prevent it spreading.

7—They threw water on the blaze. Tom Laird beat at the flames with a spade. Mrs Laird helped by filling buckets, and Peggy's little cart came in useful for rushing pails of water to the fire. Everybody worked like fury, for these haystacks were the whole winter's feeding for the farm beasts. It would be a tragedy if the hay were lost. Black Bob ran speedily to and fro with buckets of water on the cart and saved a lot of time.

8—At last they got the fire under control and saved most of the hay. " It's a good job for us you were here, Andrew," said Tom when the fire was out. Then a bark from Black Bob took Glenn over to an object lying on the ground. " Hey, Tom !" he called. " Here's what started the fire—an empty bottle !" The sun's rays had concentrated through the glass of the bottle, acting as a lens, and set the hay alight. But it might have been worse.

How running water came to Corbie

NEXT day, as Glenn and Black Bob and the Lairds walked up the burn, Tom Laird began to speak about the fire. " It was only because you were here we managed to save the hay, Andrew. It started me thinking. What I need at the croft is a better water supply. Now, how could I get water from the burn here to flow down to the trough?" " Easy !" said Glenn. " We'll build a ' flume ' to carry it down." " What's a flume?" asked Tom.

2—Glenn explained what a flume was. " It's a long trough to carry water from a river or lake to where it's needed. We could make one of timber simply enough." " Let's get begun," said Laird heartily, and the plan was started. Laird's job was to dig a trench into the high bank of the burn. Glenn started rigging up the V-shaped channel of planks which would carry the water down to the croft. Black Bob and Peggy looked on with great interest.

3—This was a tricky business the two friends were tackling, for all the seams and joints in the flume had to be leakproof. There was no sense in guiding water from the burn if it were to run all over the place from a leaky flume. But, properly made, it would save all the hard work of carrying water from the burn to the stables. Andrew Glenn was a handy man with all kinds of tools. He made a grand job of the flume. It had good tight seams.

4—Black Bob and Peggy were the keenest of onlookers when the time approached to start the flow of water into the flume as the last section of flume was set in position next to the burn. Then the great moment came when they let the water run down to the horse-trough. But when Glenn and Laird came down to watch the flow they were surprised to see it begin to trickle more and more slowly till it stopped altogether. What was wrong?

5—" Something queer about this," said Glenn. " I'm sure there's no leak in the flume." To make certain, they examined the whole length of the wooden channel and found no leaks. But when they arrived at the burn they found, to their surprise, it was almost dried up. Only pools of water remained on its gravel bed, where there had been a steady rush. " Come on, Tom," said Glenn. " Upstream we go till we find what's wrong."

6—Off they went, sticking to the bank, with Black Bob running ahead as usual. " A burn doesn't dry up as quickly as that," said Tom Laird, " unless it's been turned from its bed in some way." More than a mile from the croft they found the cause of the trouble. A great heap of stones and rubble blocked the path of the stream, which had turned off its usual course. " Landslide, looks like," remarked Glenn. " See the scar on the hillface there."

7—He pointed to a huge bare patch on the hill down which the burn flowed. It seemed as if a huge slab of rock had broken off, and in its fall dragged loose stones and earth with it, damming up the burn. " Well, it's just another job for us, Tom," said Glenn at last. " Another accident of nature, much the same as the bottle that began the haystack fire. No use worrying over it. Come on, we'll have to clear away this stoppage and free the water."

8—They didn't say much for the next hour or two, for it was arduous work clearing the stream. Both men were tired and hot when at last the burn began to flood into its usual bed. " A good job that, Tom," said Glenn when they saw the rush of water into their home-made flume. They found the trough full, and the overflow winding through a ditch and right down to the sea. Both of them felt very proud of their day's work.

The panic over Peggy

GLENN and Laird were strolling back to the house, looking forward to a meal and a rest, when they saw Mrs Laird running towards them. "Where's Peggy?" she cried. "Have you seen her? I sent her to tell you tea was ready." "When?" rapped Tom Laird. "About half an hour ago," answered his wife. Her face turned pale. "Oh, Tom," she said fearfully, "she couldn't go astray from the burn side." "Bob will find her," put in Glenn.

2—"Find Peggy, Bob," the shepherd ordered. Black Bob sniffed around and soon picked up the girl's trail. The scent led away towards the sea. Suddenly Mrs Laird exclaimed :—"There she is!" Then her voice rose to a frightened scream :—"Peggy, Peggy, come away from there!" For the little girl was right on the brink of a cliff, picking flowers. Black Bob saw her danger and raced forward. But, quick as he was, the collie was too late.

3—Peggy's head jerked up at the sound of her mother's cry. She half-turned towards them, then her foot slipped on the short turf. Over she went, to fall headlong into the water many feet below. Black Bob reached the cliff-edge and saw his little chum struggling in the sea. He didn't hesitate. He leapt over the edge and hit the water with a splash some yards away from Peggy. The little girl was swept out from the rocks even while she struggled to keep afloat.

4—There was a powerful current swirling around the rocks at that point, and when Bob came to the surface he saw Peggy being swept rapidly away from him. The collie swam furiously, but Peggy seemed to be suddenly gripped by an even stronger current. From the cliff-top Glenn and the Lairds saw there was nothing they could do to help. Peggy's life depended on Black Bob alone. But already the little girl's cries were becoming weaker.

5—For a moment Peggy was dragged under. Then her head bobbed up again. Black Bob made a terrific effort and succeeded in grabbing her frock. "He's got her!" yelled Tom Laird. "Oh, well done, Bob!" "He should get her ashore amongst the rocks," said Andrew Glenn. "Come on." They scrambled over the rocks, keeping their eyes anxiously on the struggling figures below. But suddenly Glenn dropped flat to peer over the edge.

6—"Tom," he cried anxiously. "I can't see them. They've disappeared!" Laird dropped beside him, his hand on Glenn's shoulder, his voice hoarse with fear. "Have they gone down?" he shouted. "Let me see!" He crawled nearer to the edge, craning his neck to stare down at the swirling current. There was no sign of either Peggy or Bob, and a wild panic gripped him. "Peggy! Peggy!" he shouted. Mrs Laird was pale with terror.

7—Glenn took command, for he saw that both of the Lairds were panic-stricken. "You go home, Mrs Laird," he said roughly. "Get a kettle on, heat some blankets. We'll find Peggy. Hurry, now!" And as Peggy's mother went silently away, the shepherd grasped Tom Laird's arm. "Down this way, Tom. There's still a chance they've landed in a rock crevice." He led the way to a lower ledge. But still there was no sign of Bob and Peggy.

8—Bob and Peggy could not be seen because they were trapped in a cave at sea level. The current had swept them into it, and Bob had dragged Peggy out on to a slab of rock jutting from the side of the cave. The little girl was frightened and crying. Bob began to bark loudly, trying to let his master know where they were. They were safe for the moment, but the tide was rising. Soon it would cover the slab once more.

The race against the rising tide

OUTSIDE, Andrew Glenn and Tom Laird were in a panic. They searched everywhere among the rocks but they could find no trace of Bob and Peggy. The two men climbed back on the clifftop, completely baffled by this. Then suddenly Glenn gave a shout. "Listen, Tom," he cried. Dropping to his knees, he put his ear to a crack in the rock. Faintly, from far beneath the rock, he could hear the sound of barking. "That's Bob!" Glenn cried.

2—"I couldn't mistake that bark, Tom," Glenn went on. "They're safe down there somewhere. I'll run to Corbie and get a rope." He dashed off to the croft, and within minutes was back with a long length of stout rope. They tied it firmly to a rock, and with Tom Laird holding on Glenn lowered himself over the cliff-edge. It was a dangerous business, but not new to the Selkirk shepherd. Often enough he had done it to rescue stranded sheep.

3—Glenn listened, as he climbed down, for Black Bob's guiding bark. There it came again, clearer now. And then the shepherd saw an opening in the cliff-face. Far below on the ledge in the cave Glenn saw Peggy and Bob. "They're all right, Tom," he shouted up to the crofter on top. "We'll get them out. Hang on and be ready to pull them up." But it was a grim fight against time and the rising tide for Andrew Glenn.

4—The rescue was a difficult and dangerous business. Glenn had to climb down the shaft to the cavern to get Peggy, and take her to the top before he returned for Bob. Tom helped a lot, but mostly it was a case of one-handed climbing for the daring shepherd. He handed Peggy over to her mother, who ran from the croft to meet them, and soon she was tucked up, snug and warm. It was a happy ending to Glenn's bad luck holiday.

Jack Prout continued his prolific output all during the 1939-1945 war, as well as doing his bit in the D.C.Thomson Home Guard unit. Jack is standing in the back row, second from the right. In the second row from the front, second from the right is the great Dudley D. Watkins who also served in this unit while continuing his work as an illustrator.

BIFFO THE BEAR

Everyone reading this Beano headline looked forward to meeting Biffo – except Big Eggo who was moved to a strip inside to make way for this brand new bear. Dudley D Watkins was the chosen illustrator for this likeable youngster who remained on the cover for 26 years.

Biffo, like the other Beano/Dandy cover characters, had a solid black body which editors new gave great contrast against the vivid, bold colours used on the cover.

Biffo had a human friend, a beret wearing boy called Buster. The two lived next to each other and in many issues became a comic double-act.

Biffo fronted some notable Beanos.

The highest selling Beano to date, just under 2 million copies on week 22.4.50.

The No 1000 Beano on 16.9.61.

Pictured here Biffo cuts The Beano's 25th birthday cake on 27.7.63

MEMORIES
ARE MADE OF THIS!

To mark his 90th birthday, celebrated comic artist Charlie Grigg visited the offices of DC Thomson to view some of the old Korky the Cat, Prince Whoopee and Desperate Dan pages he drew for The Dandy and Beano.

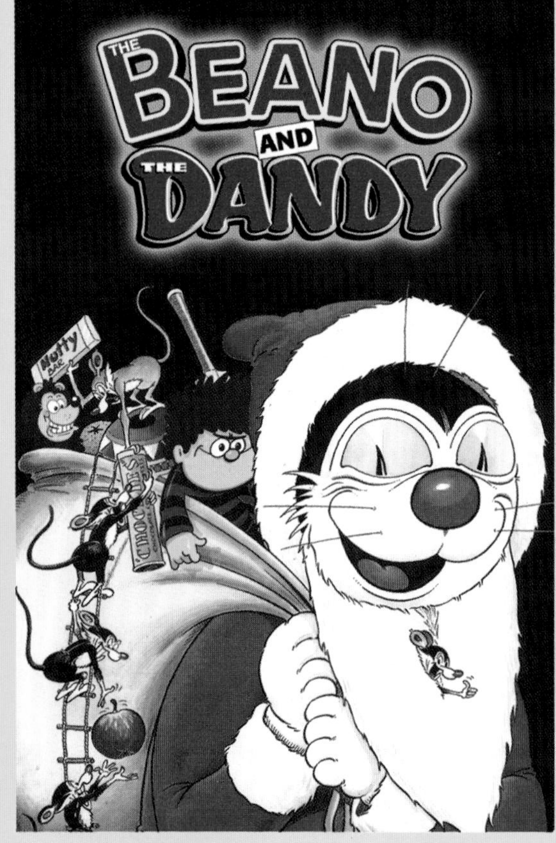
THE BEANO
AND
THE DANDY

The altered drawing.

Charlie reflects on some Korky strips he last saw on his drawing board in the sixties.

At the workstation of staff artist Jim Dewar. Jim was adding Dennis the Menace and Gnasher toys to an illustration of Korky as Santa that Charlie had done for the cover of The Dandy Annual 1968.

WILDEST WEST IN COMICS!

Little Plum and the Smellyfoot tribe first appeared in The Beano 10.10.53. Drawn by Leo Baxendale, this energetic strip was non-stop fun. The very favourite stories starred the army of crazy comic bears that lived around Plum's village. They terrorised and outsmarted the Smellyfeet in the most ingenious comic ways.

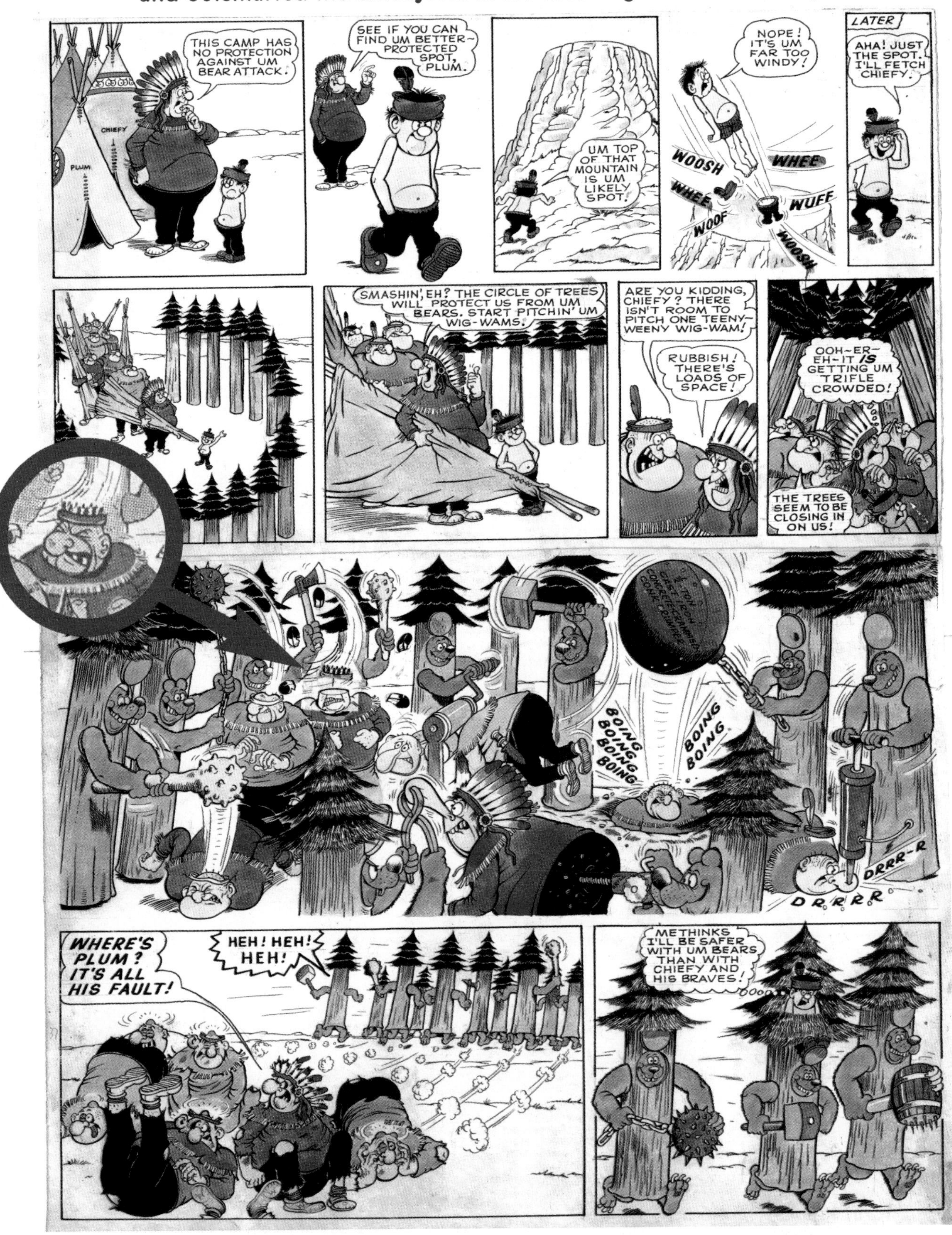

The artist had comically beheaded one of the tribe but the Editor must have taken cold feet, for by the time it appeared in print the brave had a head.

In 1960 The Beano got artist Leo Baxendale to illustrate the front cover topline. He used Plum and the bears to do a wonderful series of little comic cameos.

KEEP TUNED IN TO "THE BEANO"!
THE BEANO
No. 923—Mar. 26th, 1960.
2D
EVERY THURSDAY
HO-HO!
HA-HA!
HA-HO!
"The BEANO" Is Good For You!
THE BEANO
No. 925—Apr. 9th, 1960.
2D
EVERY THURSDAY
CASTOR OIL
CHARGE!
HEH! HEH! THAT FOOLED 'EM. THE BUFFALOES THINK THEY'VE GOT RID OF ME NOW!
ME PUT THIS MODEL ON UM BEAR'S FOOTBALL GROUND!
LATER
STOP THIS ONE, PLUM!
HE-HE! THE BEARS WILL THINK THEY'VE GOT RID OF ME, TOO!
NOW FOR UM FINAL PART OF MY PLAN!
WAH! IT'S PLUM'S GHOST!
IT'S PLUM'S GHOST!
NOW FOR UM BEARS!
HA! HA! ME SCARED AWAY ALL UM BUFFALOES AND BEARS!
DID YOU?
GOSH! UM BEARS HAVE TAKEN OVER UM CAMP. THEY'RE SCARED TO GO BACK TO UM CAVES!
BACK TO UM CACTUS PLANT!

KEEP AN EYE ON "THE BEANO" EVERY THURSDAY
THE BEANO
No. 931—May 21st, 1960.
2D
EVERY THURSDAY
BE SMART~BE A "BEANO" READER
THE BEANO
No. 936—June 25th, 1960.
2D
EVERY THURSDAY
PLUM'S JUST PAID 200 DOLLARS FOR A CAR HE'S NEVER SEEN, NOW HE'S WAITING FOR THE CAR DEALER TO DELIVER IT
LITTLE PLUM
HERE IT COMES NOW!
I WONDER HOW SOON I'LL GET SOMETHING IN MY BEAR TRAP?
LITTLE PLUM
ALL MINE FOR UM 200 DOLLARS!
YOUR CAR'S IN THE BOOT, PLUM!
THAT'S A CAR??
WHAT DO YOU EXPECT FOR 200 DOLLARS?
I'LL START UP AND GIVE IT UM TRIAL RUN!
HUNTER
BEAR TRAP
WHOOSH
ROAR

This classic Beano Book set from 1958 is about cars but if you look carefully there are funny little asides with the wild west creatures going on all through the strip.

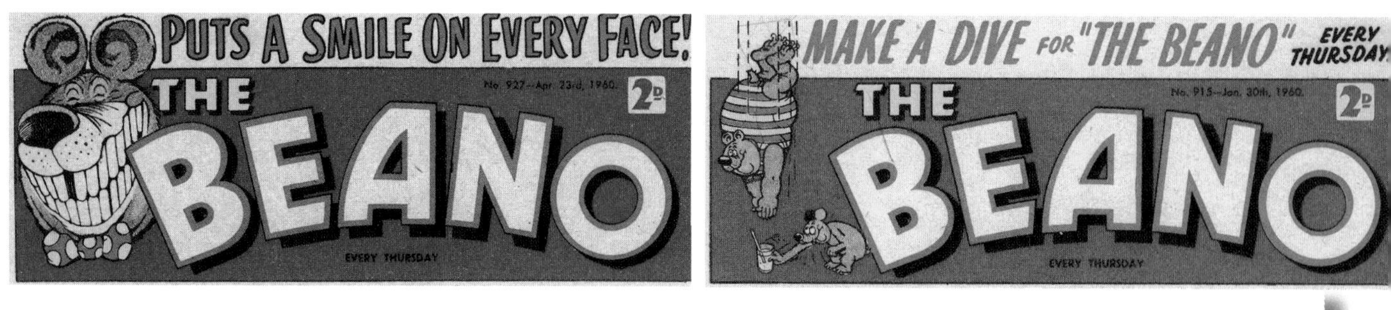

The vulture gets the laughs twice in these highly visual pages.

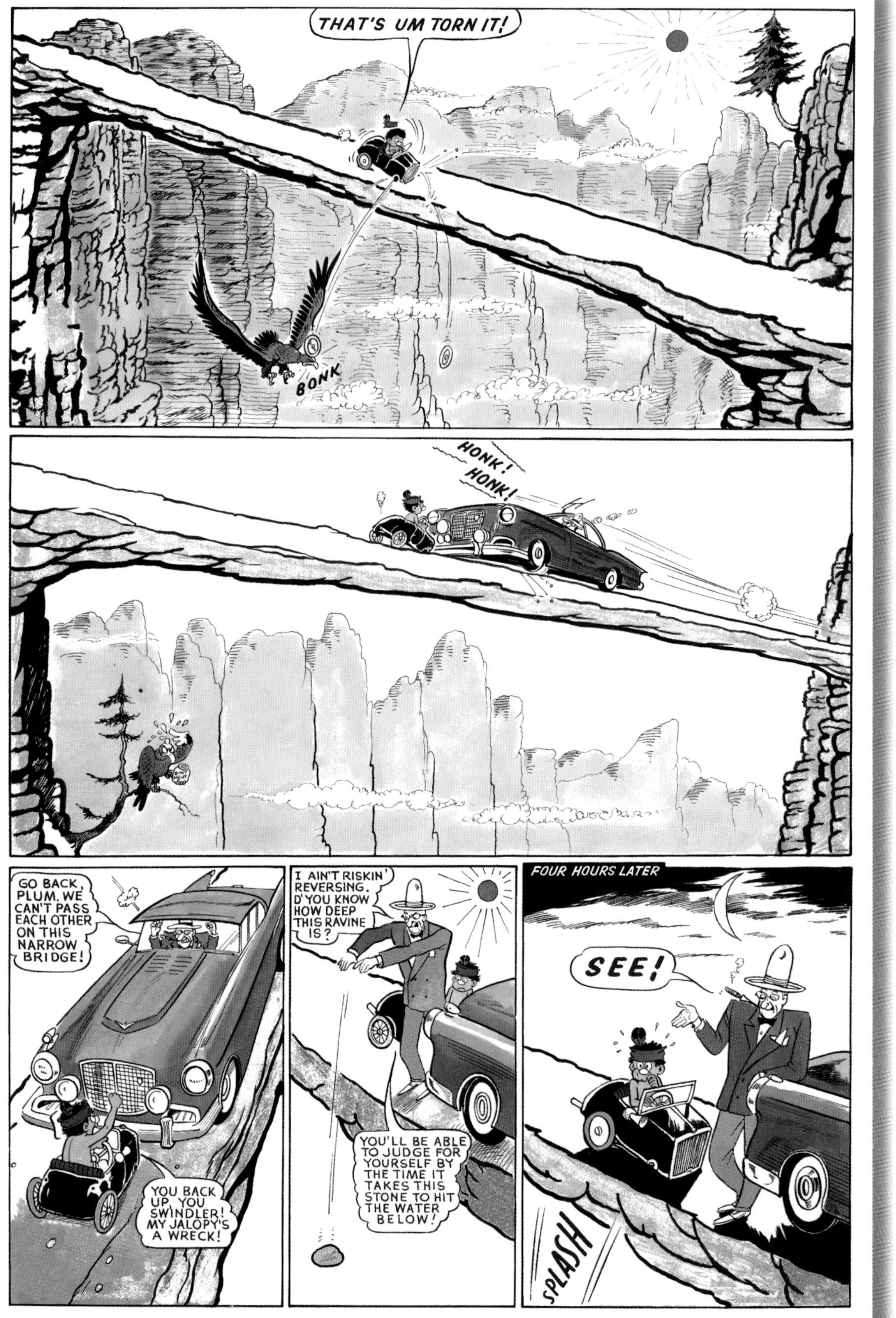

This elaborate bear trap was one of the best laughs in the Beano Book that year.

The famous sausages title block from 1960.

Week 1 and the Bears in natural fur.

The bears were very popular, so in June 1959 a new page was launched for a 4 week trial – it starred Ma, Pa and Teddy Bear and was called simply The Three Bears.

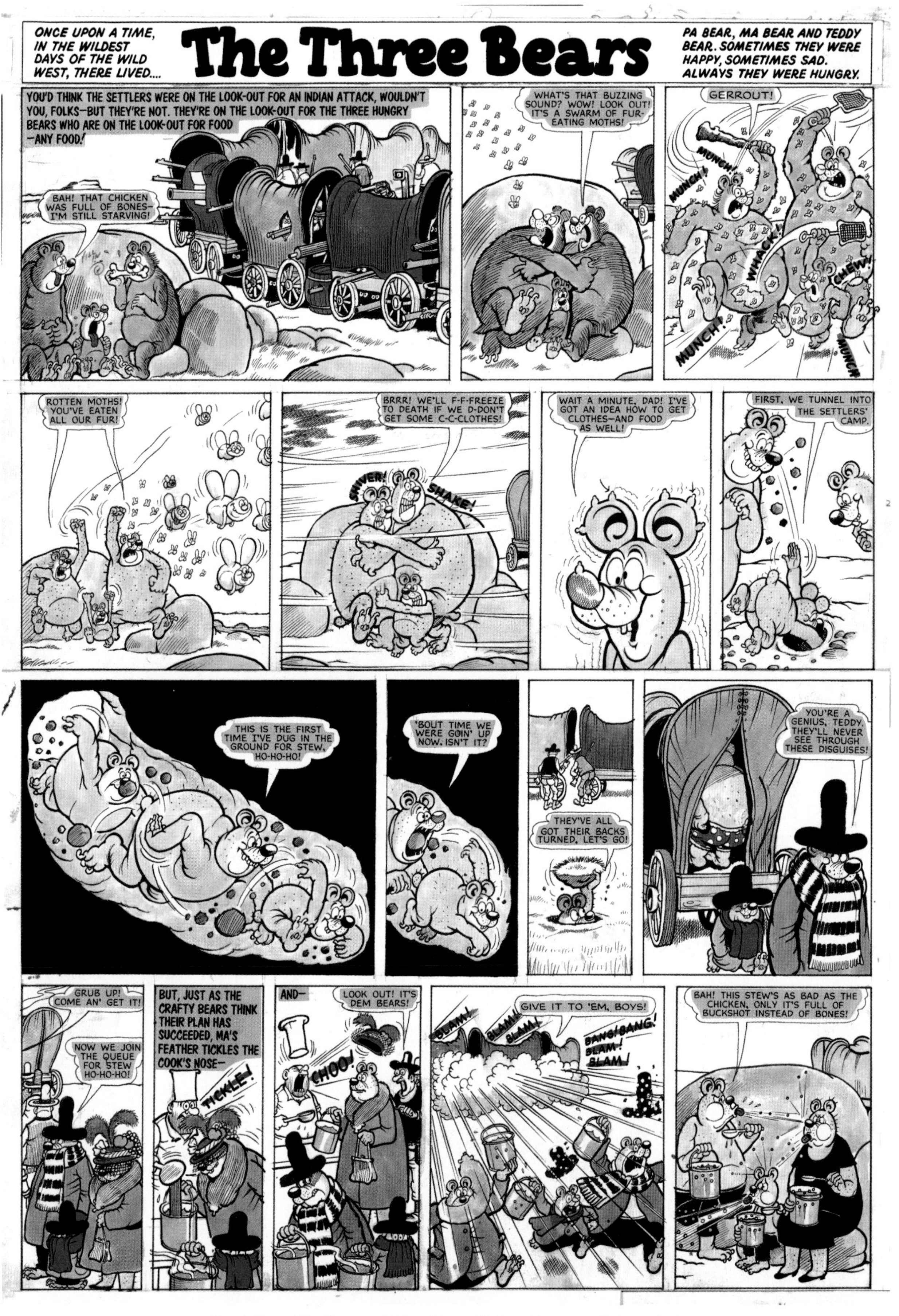

Week 2 and the Bears get the clothes that will become their costume.

The Beano editor was deluged with requests to see the Bears again. In October 1960 they returned and ran continuously until 1985.

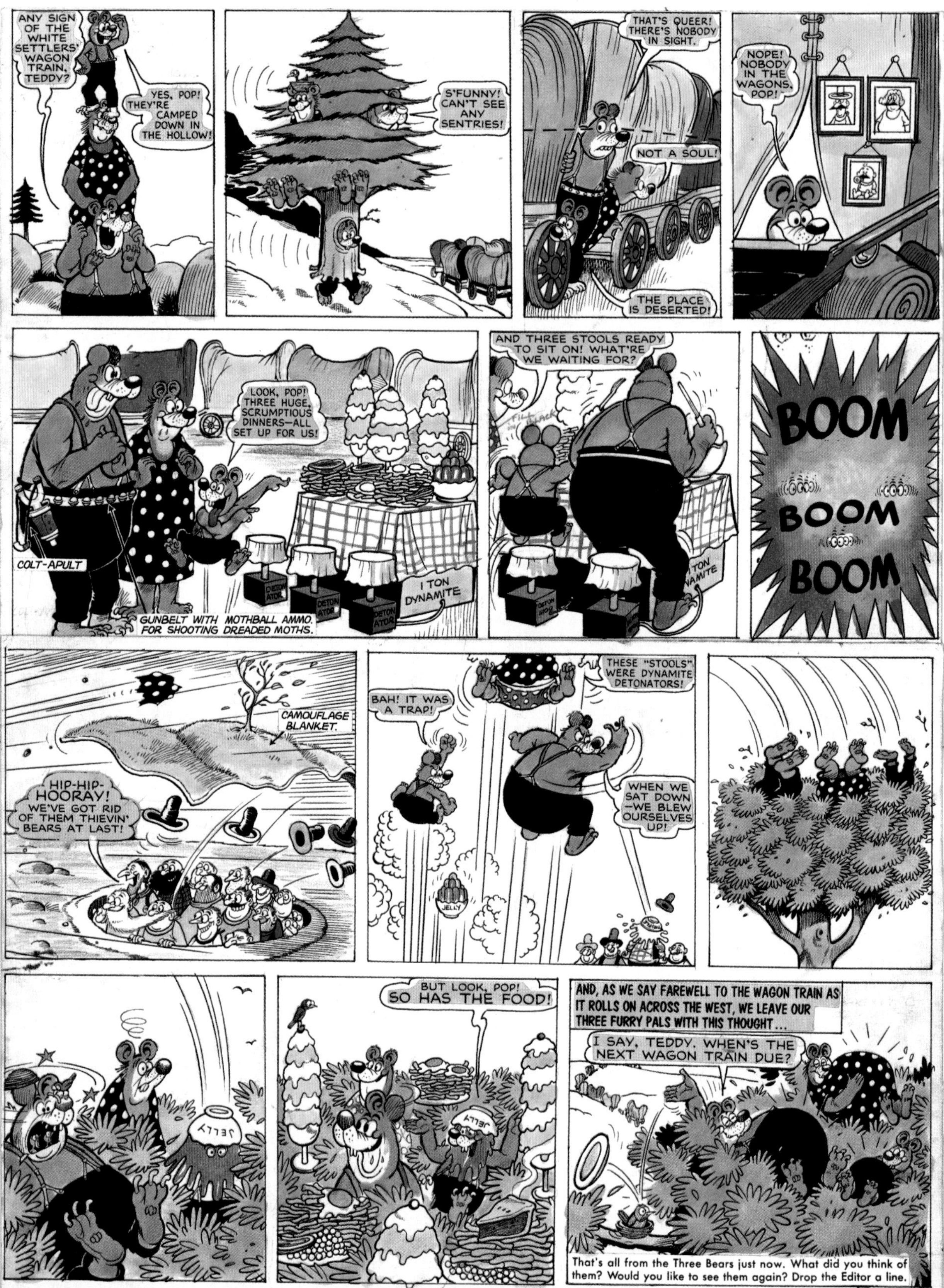

PETS' PICTURE GALLERY
ANIMAL ANTICS
Bus Stop
traveline
ARE YOU SURE THIS IS THE STOP FOR HORSE GUARDS PARADE?
THUMPER SEEMED TO HAVE AN IDENTITY CRISIS
WHO PEED IN MY BATH?
CALL THAT A BEARD?
A WORD IN YOUR EAR SUNSHINE!
CALL THAT A BEARD?

Creature DIScomforts! Corporal Clott and Dennis the Menace.

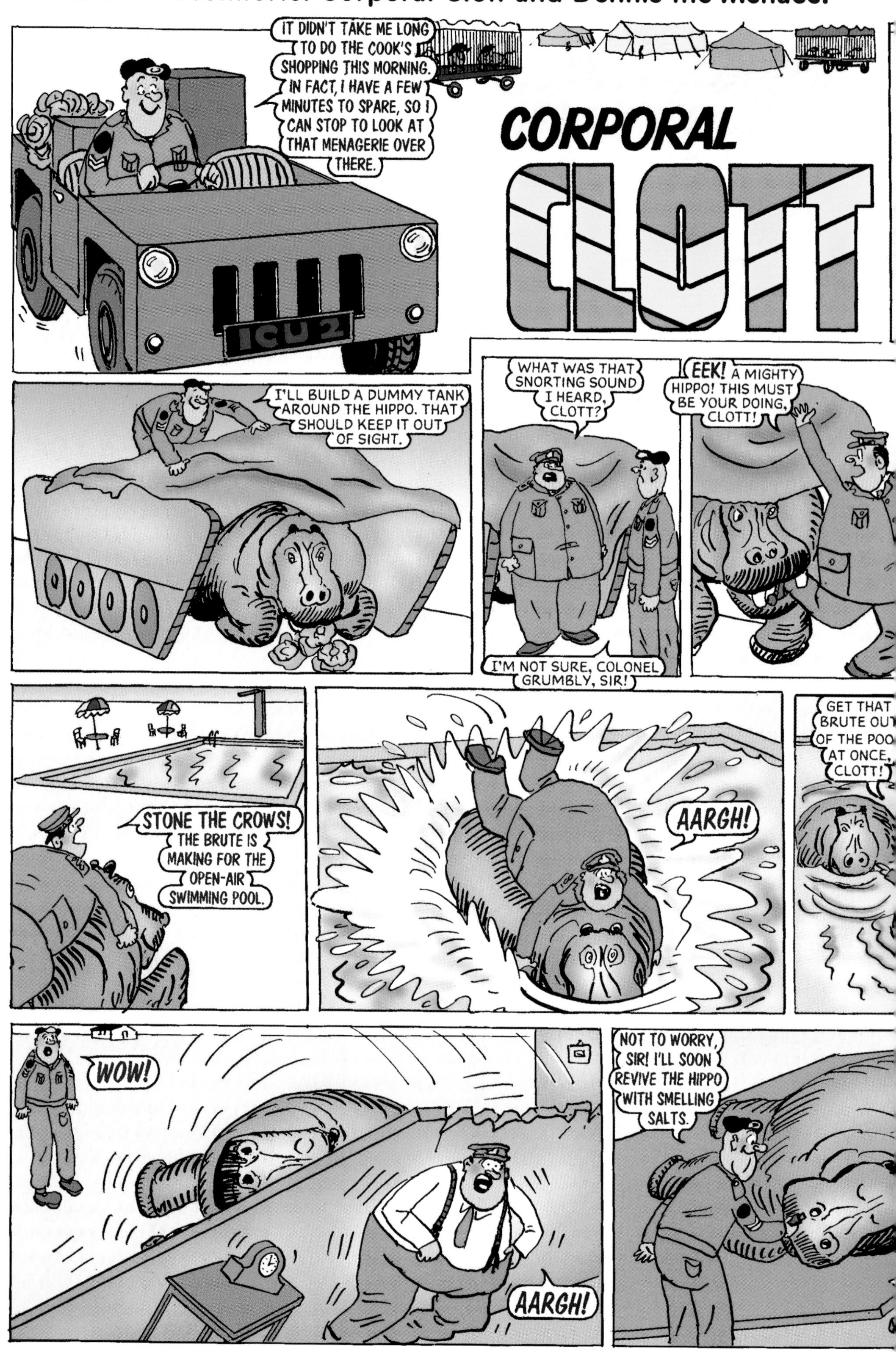

Both strips were first illustrated by Beano/Dandy artist David Law.

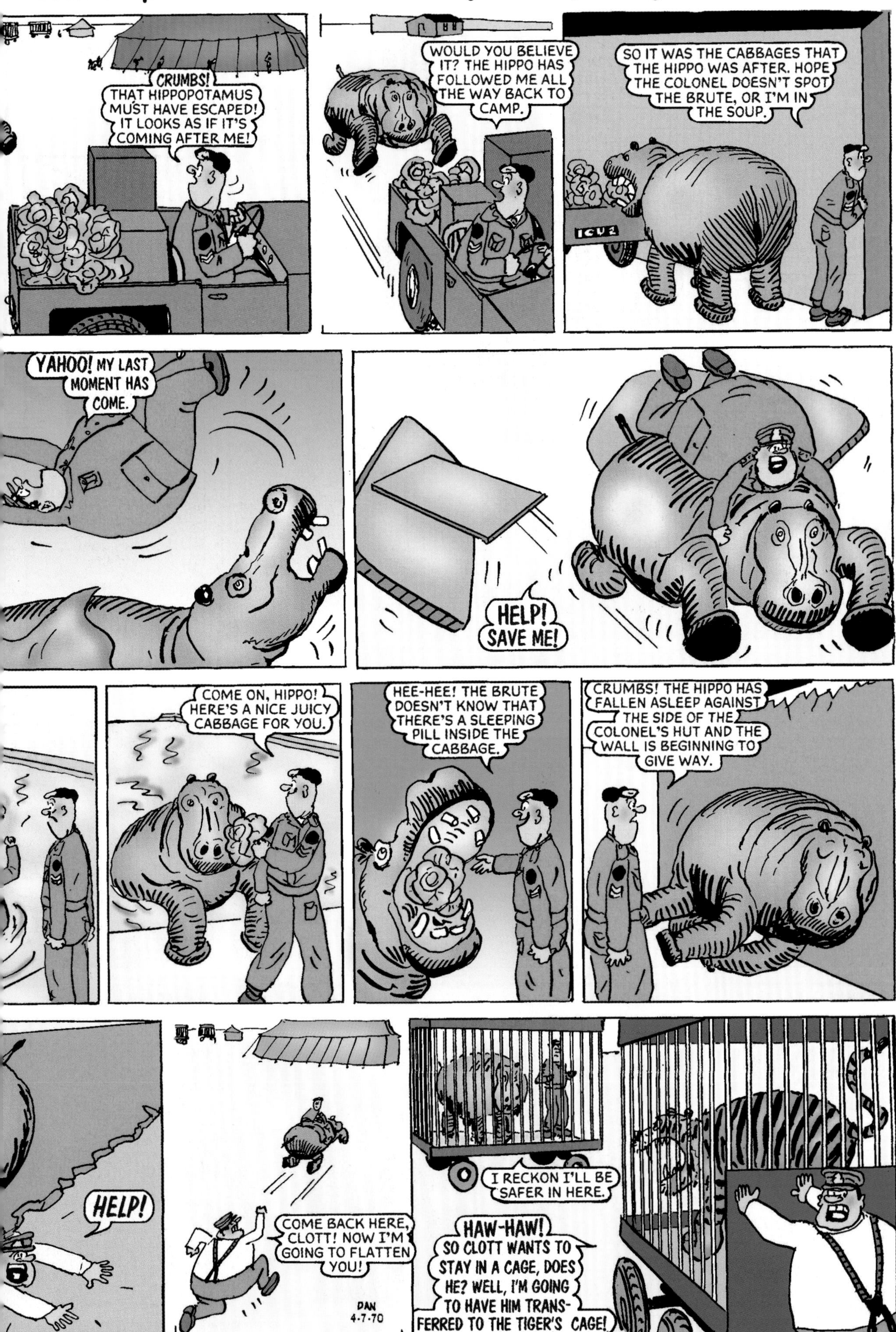

Note: A guinea was equal to £1.05.

HORSE PLAY
YOU'RE ALWAYS UP TO MISCHIEF AND GETTING DIRTY! WHY DON'T YOU SETTLE DOWN AND THINK ABOUT YOUR FUTURE CAREER?
SO DENNIS DOES–
COLLEGE PUD
I MIGHT BE A CANNIBAL!
SCHOOL
OR I MIGHT BE A DEMOLITION EXPERT!
GOOD! HERE'S A CHANCE TO PRACTISE A CAREER–I'LL BE A COALMAN!
LAUNDRY
THIS IS EASY! THE OLD HORSE KNOWS ALL THE STOPS–I JUST HAVE TO UNLOAD THE COAL!
UP WITH THE COAL-HATCH–
–AND DOWN SHE GOES!
SILLY DENNIS! THIS IS THE COAL-HATCH OVER HERE!
ARGH! OUR SPOTLESS LINEN!
RUMBLE!
CRASH!
HEH! HEH! SUCH FUN–NOW TO MAKE A QUICK GETAWAY!
KINDLY CUSTOMERS GIVE THE COALMAN'S HORSE TIT-BITS, BUT -
I'LL TAKE THAT–CHOMP!
RAGE
SNATCH
SOON THE POLICE ARE ON DENNIS'S TRAIL
HAA! GET ON, THERE!
LITTLE DOES DENNIS KNOW THAT HIS HORSE IS ALSO PLANNING A NEW CAREER FOR ITSELF–AS A GRAND-NATIONAL JUMPER!
AND IT STARTS PRACTISING SRAIGHT AWAY-
ZIP!
CRASH!
HELP!
SOMEBODY GET ME OUT OF HERE!
RIGHT AWAY, DENNIS!
...AND BACK AT THE YARD THERE ARE ANOTHER TWENTY BAGS WAITING TO BE DELIVERED!
GROAN!

Bird brain antics from Clott. JC Hughes was the artist.

He was better known for his Bully Beef and Chips strips.

MAN-MADE MAYHEM!!

Not all our crazy creatures were flesh and blood...take a look at these wonderful creations.

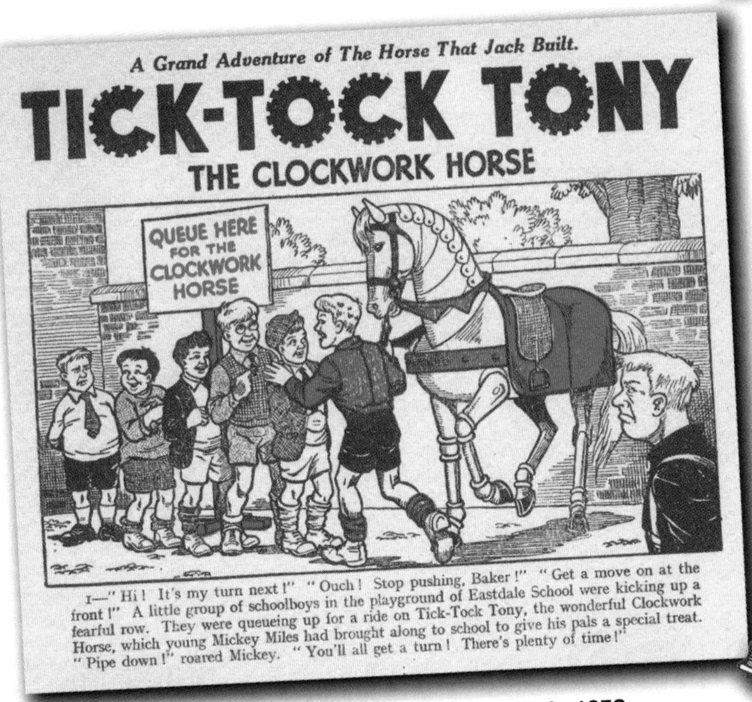

A Grand Adventure of The Horse That Jack Built.
TICK-TOCK TONY
THE CLOCKWORK HORSE
QUEUE HERE FOR THE CLOCKWORK HORSE
1—" Hi! It's my turn next!" "Ouch! Stop pushing, Baker!" "Get a move on at the front!" A little group of schoolboys in the playground of Eastdale School were kicking up a fearful row. They were queueing up for a ride on Tick-Tock Tony, the wonderful Clockwork Horse, which young Mickey Miles had brought along to school to give his pals a special treat. "Pipe down!" roared Mickey. "You'll all get a turn! There's plenty of time!"

Tick–Tock–Tony galloped onto the Beano pages in 1950.

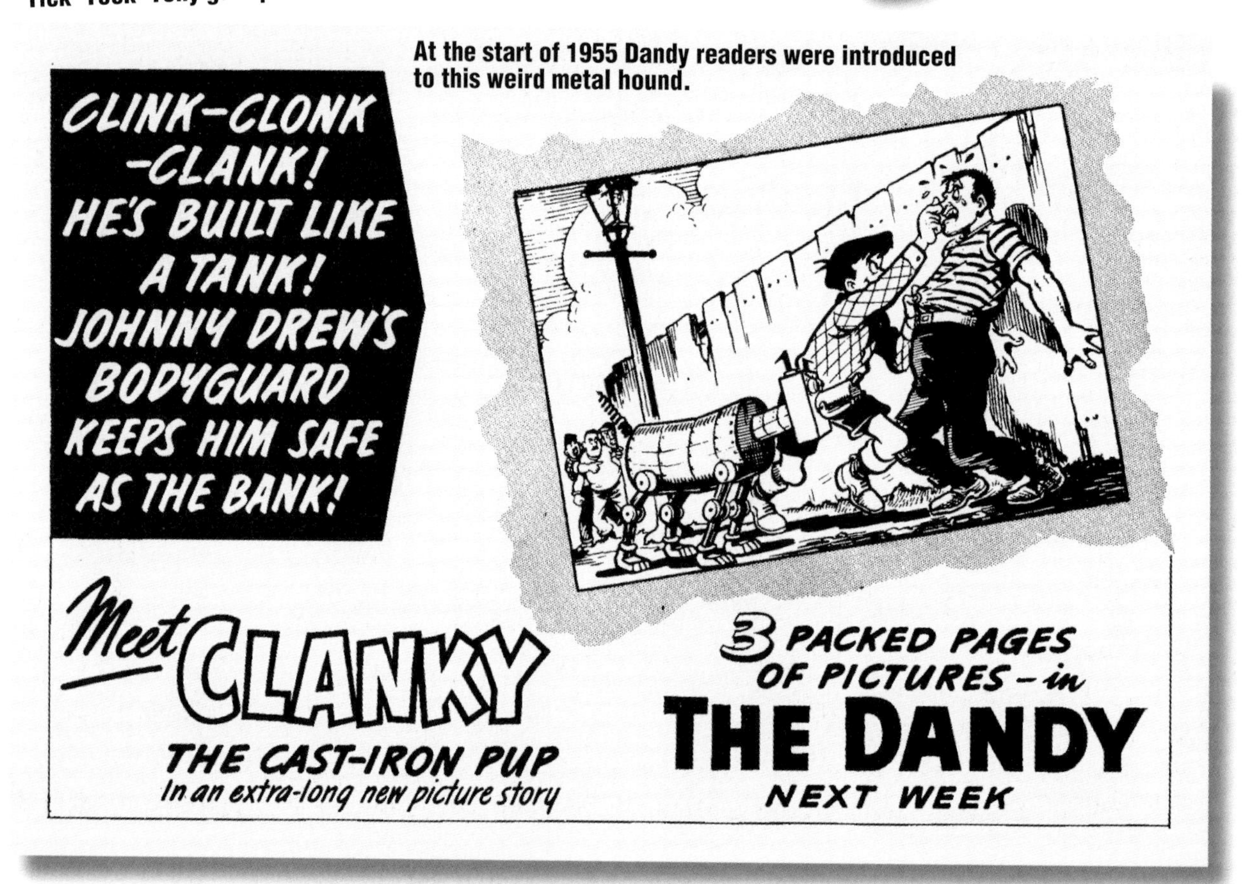

CLINK-CLONK -CLANK! HE'S BUILT LIKE A TANK! JOHNNY DREW'S BODYGUARD KEEPS HIM SAFE AS THE BANK!

In an extra-long new picture story
3 PACKED PAGES OF PICTURES – in

At the start of 1955 Dandy readers were introduced to this weird metal hound.

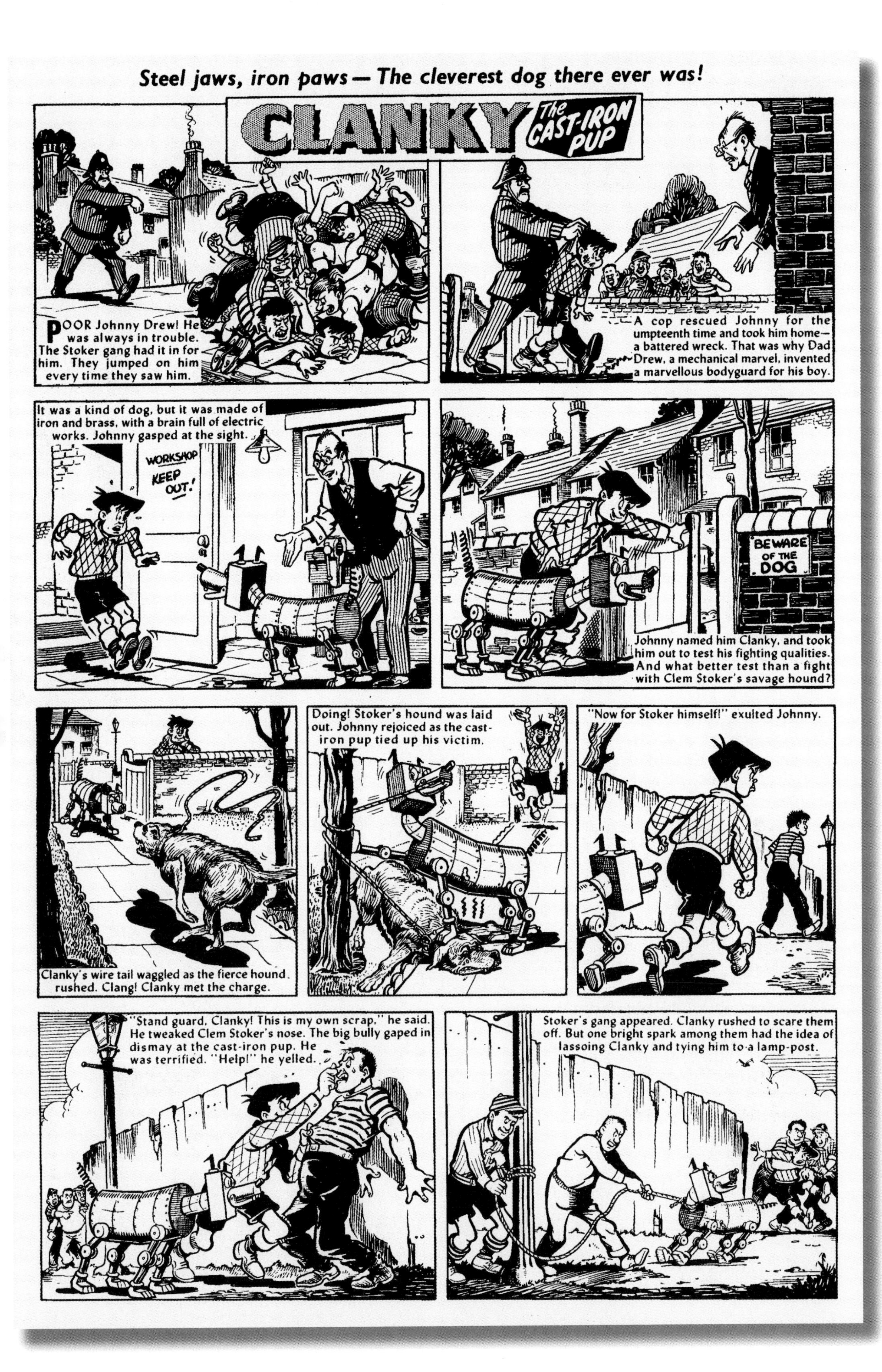
Steel jaws, iron paws — The cleverest dog there ever was!
CLANKY The CAST-IRON PUP
POOR Johnny Drew! He was always in trouble. The Stoker gang had it in for him. They jumped on him every time they saw him.
A cop rescued Johnny for the umpteenth time and took him home—a battered wreck. That was why Dad Drew, a mechanical marvel, invented a marvellous bodyguard for his boy.
It was a kind of dog, but it was made of iron and brass, with a brain full of electric works. Johnny gasped at the sight.
WORKSHOP KEEP OUT!
BEWARE OF THE DOG
Johnny named him Clanky, and took him out to test his fighting qualities. And what better test than a fight with Clem Stoker's savage hound?
Clanky's wire tail waggled as the fierce hound rushed. Clang! Clanky met the charge.
Doing! Stoker's hound was laid out. Johnny rejoiced as the cast-iron pup tied up his victim.
"Now for Stoker himself!" exulted Johnny.
"Stand guard, Clanky! This is my own scrap," he said. He tweaked Clem Stoker's nose. The big bully gaped in dismay at the cast-iron pup. He was terrified. "Help!" he yelled.
Stoker's gang appeared. Clanky rushed to scare them off. But one bright spark among them had the idea of lassoing Clanky and tying him to a lamp-post.

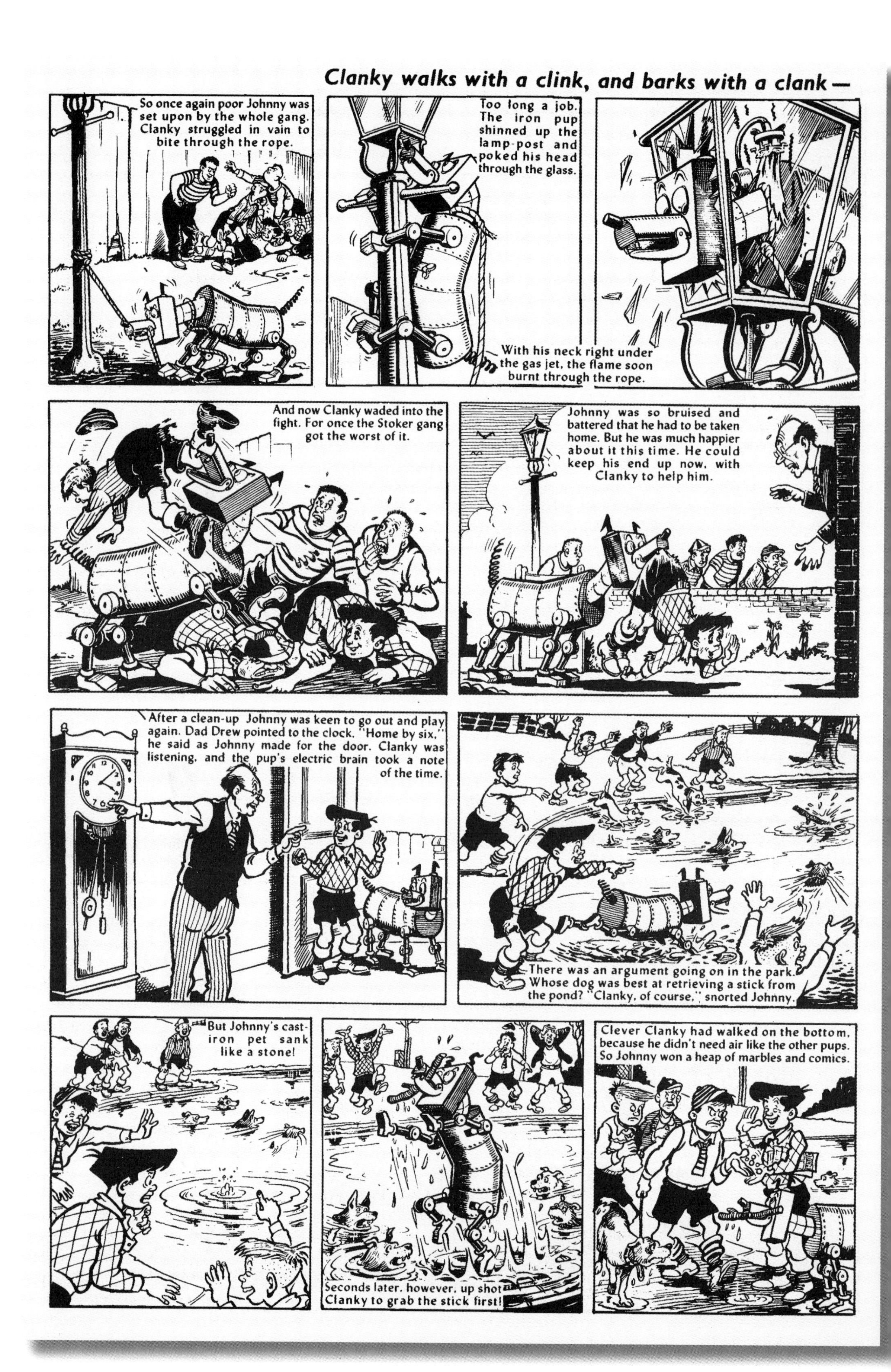
Clanky walks with a clink, and barks with a clank—
So once again poor Johnny was set upon by the whole gang. Clanky struggled in vain to bite through the rope.
Too long a job. The iron pup shinned up the lamp-post and poked his head through the glass.
With his neck right under the gas jet, the flame soon burnt through the rope.
And now Clanky waded into the fight. For once the Stoker gang got the worst of it.
Johnny was so bruised and battered that he had to be taken home. But he was much happier about it this time. He could keep his end up now, with Clanky to help him.
After a clean-up Johnny was keen to go out and play again. Dad Drew pointed to the clock. "Home by six," he said as Johnny made for the door. Clanky was listening, and the pup's electric brain took a note of the time.
There was an argument going on in the park. Whose dog was best at retrieving a stick from the pond? "Clanky, of course," snorted Johnny.
But Johnny's cast-iron pet sank like a stone!
Seconds later, however, up shot Clanky to grab the stick first!
Clever Clanky had walked on the bottom, because he didn't need air like the other pups. So Johnny won a heap of marbles and comics.

He's a pup who can think, and he's built like a tank.

The next argument was about catching rabbits. Clanky didn't do so well. The rabbits disappeared underground, and Clanky didn't fancy digging for them.
But the cast-iron pup's brain got to work. He knew where rabbits were easy to get. Certainly these rabbits were white, but Clanky darkened them — with soot!
One by one he brought the "wild" rabbits to his master. Once again the lads admitted defeat. They handed over more sweets and toys and more comics.
Then Tommy Jenkins discovered where those dark rabbits had come from—his own hutch of tame bunnies! Johnny and Clanky scrammed.
The boys chased after them. One of them clonked Clanky with a turf. But Johnny bribed a kid to lend him his trike.
Clanky pedalled and steered. Johnny used a mop like a lance, and he mopped up his opponents.
Disaster! The trike battered into Johnny's own garden gate. The two soared through the air—
—and clean through the sitting-room window! But Clanky stretched out a triumphant paw at the clock. The hands were dead on six. Johnny's cast-iron pup had brought him home on time. Dad gaped at his battered son. He was beginning to wonder whether Clanky had been a good invention!

Trouble afoot on Christmas Day—When a robber snatches Puss's boots away!

Two bobbies really lose their rag—When they see what's in this bully's bag!
GET HIM, BUSTER!
Once again Tomtin was unable to run, but this time the cat started scrambling up a tree.
Tomtin would have made it, if Buster hadn't snatched him by the tail.
SWAG
Buster Brass held Tomtin down while his master stole the boots.
SNIGGER! FANCY A PUSS-IN-BOOTS WITH NO BOOTS!
YOU ROTTEN BULLY, HARPER!
SWAG
But as soon as Tomtin was on his feet again, he scampered off and fetched yet another pair!
HEY! YOU! LET'S SEE WHAT YOU'VE GOT IN THAT SACK!
The mystery of where all the boots came from was solved when two bootless bobbies came running from the police station.
One look at Horace in his burglar's outfit was enough for the furious policemen. They thought he must be the boot-stealer!
The bobbies didn't see Freddie tying together the boots Tomtin had just brought.
SWAG
YOU DON'T WANT TO BE CAUGHT WITH THESE BOOTS NOW, TOMTIN.
HARPER COLLECTS BOOTS, AND HE CAN HAVE THEM.
Freddie sent the boots spinning through the air and Horace yelped as they twirled round his ankles and brought him down.
SWAG
YIKE!
SWAG
YEEAGH!
I WOULDN'T LIKE TO BE IN HARPER'S BOOTS NOW! HE'S FOR IT!
Freddie was right, for when Horace's swag bag was emptied the other stolen boots were found. The bully would have some explaining to do in the police station!
Freddie got Tomtin's fancy dress boots back from the bobbies before the robber was marched off.
SERVES THE BIG BULLY RIGHT! HE'LL MISS THE PARTY NOW.
DAN 27.12.75
HURRAY!
MERRY CHRISTMAS, EVERYBODY!
A MECHANICAL PUSS-IN-BOOTS. WHATEVER NEXT?
GRAND XMAS FANCY DRESS PARTY
Tomtin had had to battle against the odds just like Puss-in-Boots in the story. That's why he got a special cheer when he arrived at the party.

STARTING NOW—The amazing story of a boy who roams the Pacific in a giant metal swordfish which can swim, leap, and fight like a real swordfish !
DEEP-SEA DANNY'S
IRON FISH

Perhaps you though some of the adventure stories that appeared in The Beano and Dandy were too wildly imaginative or even bizarre? In 1949 a story began in The Beano called Deep Sea Danny's Iron Fish. The story involved young Danny Gray and his adventures as pilot of a fantastic mechanical swordfish...stretching credibility too far? Pictured here is an American invention of the late 1990s called Seabreacher, manufactured by Innespace almost fifty years after the iron fish made its debut!

1963 Korky was the winner -

- And his prize a dog's dinner!

Horse laughs with Dan. Though not signed, the strip was drawn by Dudley D. Watkins.

Dan loves his horse, it must be said — Except when it occupies his bed!

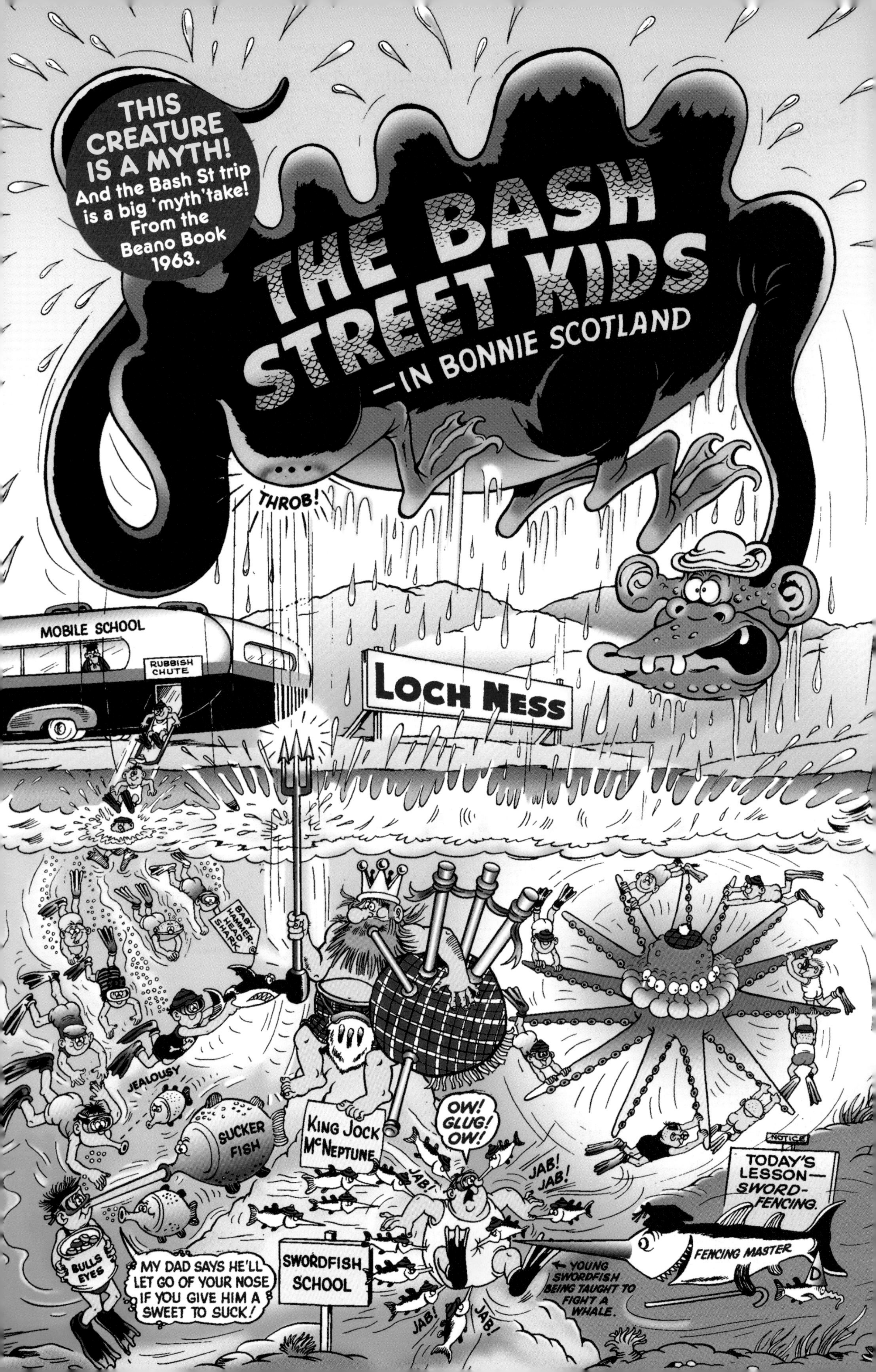
THIS CREATURE IS A MYTH! And the Bash St trip is a big 'myth'take! From the Beano Book 1963.
THE BASH STREET KIDS
—IN BONNIE SCOTLAND
THROB!
MOBILE SCHOOL
RUBBISH CHUTE
LOCH NESS
BABY HAMMER-HEAD SHARK
JEALOUSY
SUCKER FISH
KING JOCK McNEPTUNE
OW! GLUG! OW!
JAB!
JAB! JAB!
NOTICE
TODAY'S LESSON— SWORD-FENCING.
BULLS EYES
MY DAD SAYS HE'LL LET GO OF YOUR NOSE IF YOU GIVE HIM A SWEET TO SUCK!
SWORDFISH SCHOOL
← YOUNG SWORDFISH BEING TAUGHT TO FIGHT A WHALE.
FENCING MASTER
JAB!
JAB!

Removal (cara)van!
NO, FOLKS! IT ISN'T A COLLECTION OF LINES WRITTEN BY THE BASH STREET KIDS—
—IT'S A COLLECTION OF PETITIONS WRITTEN BY THE GOOD CITIZENS OF THE BASH STREET AREA ASKING FOR THE KIDS TO BE REMOVED.
BAN THE BASH ST KIDS!
GIVE US A BREAK!
BASH ST KIDS SCRAM!
EITHER THEY GO, OR WE GO!
THE BASH ST KIDS MUST GO!
SEND THEM AWAY— ANYWHERE!
PLEASE BANISH THE BASH ST KIDS
BASH ST KIDS GET OUT
SO, NEXT MORNING AT THE LOCAL COACH-BUILDER'S FACTORY-
YES, GENTLEMEN, WE CAN LET YOU HAVE WHAT YOU WANT—IT WILL ARRIVE THIS AFTERNOON!
THIS IS "IT."
BASH STREET MOBILE SCHOOL
YOU, TEACHER, WILL TAKE THE CHILDREN ON AN EDUCATIONAL TRIP—AND THE FURTHER AWAY THE BETTER!
AT LAST! THIS IS THE MOMENT THE CITIZENS HAVE BEEN WAITING FOR.
HOO-OOT!
CHEERS!
HOORAY!
BASH STREET MOBILE SCHOOL
LET US OUT!
HOI!
YAH!
BOO!
ROTTERS!
HISS!
HOORAY!
CHUG! CHUG!
FIVE MILLION "CHUG-CHUGS" LATER, THE KIDS ARRIVE IN SCOTLAND.
LOCH NESS
THIS LOOKS AS GOOD A PLACE AS ANY.
D-DING-D-DING!
SCHOOL BELL
DING-DING!
THE BELL! CHARGE, KIDS!

Awful eye-full!
BASH STREET MOBILE SCHOOL
SUFFERIN' SPORRANS! IT'S THE BASH STREET KIDS!
LOCH NESS
LOCH NESS MONSTER
AGGH! LET ME OOT O' HERE! I'VE JUST SEEN A HORRIBLE SICHT—A LADDIE WI' LONG EARS AN' A MOUTH LIKE A BULLDOZER!
LOCH NESS
JOHN O' GROATS
HAGGIS WARREN
MAN, THE TADPOLES ARE GROWIN' AWFY BIG THIS YEAR!
AS SOON AS YOU GET DRIED OUT, WE'RE GOING TO VISIT THE LOCAL HIGHLAND GAMES!

Bent tent!
PEAS
SMASHIN'! A MACHINE-GUN PEASHOOTER!
PING! PING! PING! PING!
BAGPIPE BLOWING CONTEST.
THUD!
BOING!
BITE
HAGGIS
MACOOYAH!
CRUNCH!
DANNY HELPS THE HAMMER-THROWERS TO GET A FIRMER GRIP.
HAMMER-THROWERS' HAMMERS
DO NOT TOUCH OR YOU WILL GET HAMMERED!
TINY MACTICH'S HAMMER
ECK MACFLUNG'S
GLUE
RIP-P!
TUT-TUT, LADDIE! YE'RE MEANT TAE COME IN THROUGH THE DOOR, YE KEN!
CRASH!
MACTEA TENT
PORRIDGE
TEA
THIS IS THE FAMOUS MACTRUNK CABER. IT HAS NEVER BEEN TOSSED BEFORE.
I'LL GIVE THAT BLOKE A HELPING HAND!
PUFF! OOP!
UGH! AGH!
GASP! GRUNT!
EEAGH! PUFF!
UH!
TWANG!
CREAK!

WELL, IT'S BEEN TOSSED NOW – RIGHT INTO THE PRIZES TENT.
HOO-OOCH!
CRASH!
SMASH!
PRIZES TENT
CRUNCH!
CONVULSIVE TWITCH!

Cattle battlers!
YE SASSENACHS HAVE RUINED THE GAMES! AH'LL GET MA WILD HIGHLANDERS TAE DEAL WI' YE!
RUBBISH DUMP
YAH! FAT HAGGIS!
CLANG!
1ST PRIZE
WE'RE NOT FRIGHTENED OF YOUR WILD HIGHLANDERS, YOU SCOTCH EGG!—OUR BRAVE ENGLISH TEACHER WILL BASH 'EM EASILY!
RA-AZ-Z-Z!
ER—GULP!—NOW DON'T BE HASTY, CHILDREN!
CHARGE, LADS! REMEMBER BANNOCKBURN!
SNORT! BELLOW!
STOMP!
HELP! MUM!
RUMBLE!
BELLOW!
SNORT!
TRAMPLE!
GRUNT!
EEK! WHEN HE SAID, "WILD HIGHLANDERS," HE MEANT WILD HIGHLAND CATTLE!
AGH-H! PREPARE FOR RAPID RETREAT!

The monster eats Bash Street sweets!
THAE SASSENACHS HAVE ESCAPED, HAMISH–JUST WHEN WE WERE ABOOT TAE SPIFFLICATE THEM!
HAVE YE SEEN THAE BASH STREET BRATS, JOHN?
NA, MAN, NA!
JOHN
JOHN O' GROATS
LOCH NESS MONSTER'S HOLIDAY CAVERN
MONSTER HUMBUGS
GLUG!–GLUGGLE!–WE'VE HAD TO GIVE THE ROTTEN OL' MONSTER OUR SWEET SUPPLY TO KEEP IT HAPPY!
WELL, WE WON'T BE WELCOME IN SCOTLAND, NOW. WHERE DO WE GO FROM HERE?.... READERS–YOU CAN FIND OUT WHERE LATER IN THIS BOOK!

THE ART OF PADDY BRENNAN

Paddy Brennan began drawing for The Dandy in September 1949 with the series, Sir Solomon Snoozer. Here is shown a small selection of the wonderful creatures and characters he drew.

The boy with the pet who actually dares
To go and rub noses with the fiercest bears!

Willie Willikin was the proud master of the queerest pets ever seen on earth. They had come to him from nobody knew where, perhaps from another world, in a strange flying machine. Willie always rode on the back of his favourite, the Pobble, while the snake WUM and the Big Bong Bird were never far away. The Bong Bird had four chicks and at this moment they were up to mischief. Here was young Mary Martin pushing her doll's pram along the street. The Bong chicks took a fancy for a ride in Mary's pram – and here's how they set about getting one.

Deep snores echoed through a cave in the heart of England. Most of them came from a man dressed in armour of the Middle Ages. But it wasn't shining armour! There was dust, cobwebs and spiders everywhere, even in the man's straggly beard and the plume of his helmet. The horse that snored beside him wore faded trappings and a peculiar high saddle. And the third sleeper, a long-haired boy, wore the tight-fitting breeches and jerkin of an old-time page-boy.

The three of them looked as though they had slept a very long time – when a sudden and tremendous, ear-splitting, shattering explosion shook the cave, and a rushing blast of wind swept away dust and cobwebs and spiders and all. "Eh, what's that, Roger?" said the man, awaking with a jerk. "Gadzooks! We must have slept for many hours!" Hours indeed! Sir Solomon was due for a shock. He and his horse and his page-boy had been asleep for hundreds of years.

Exerting every ounce of his tremendous strength the strong-man heaved –
The SHIPWRECKED CIRCUS
CRUSOE ISLAND, an uncharted stretch of land in the South Seas, is the home of the world's strangest castaways—the stars of Samson's Circus. It is many months since their ship, the Margo, was wrecked off the island. Since then, not a day passes without the circus folk practising their acts in the hope that one day they will leave Crusoe Island and perform all over the world.
But one morning, little Gloopy the clown, and Horace the educated ape, decided to go fishing instead of practising.
THE ISLAND OF MONSTERS
DAVIE DUNBAR fled, and it was a nightmare flight. Chasing him a was a hedgehog—a hedgehog as big as a horse! Strange things had happened on this little island where Davie had spent all his life. His father, the storekeeper, had sailed away for supplies weeks ago, and in that time extraordinary changes had come over all the little animals and insects of the island.
Every one of them had grown to enormous size. There were wasps like eagles, beetles as big as tigers—and now this giant hedgehog! The natives had fled from the island. It was completely deserted by human beings, except for Davie and his faithful helper, a native named Krambo.
Bewildered by these strange happenings, but determined to guard his Dad's store, Davie had, with Krambo's help, built a stockade around it. He was making for it now, carrying the stem of bananas he had ventured out to cut. He yelled for Krambo as he pounded along, with the giant hedgehog making up on him fast.

The BIRD BOY
Look, Harrk! That man is going to shoot a baby seal!
The huge white albatross wheeled in the chill air above the gleaming, icy wastes of the Antarctic, before swooping low towards a whaling ship. Clinging to the scaly legs of the enormous bird was a boy, clad in a single garment of pleated bird feathers. This was Kelvin the Bird Boy who had lived most of his life in these icy wastes.
We have updated with colour and speech this story from the 1957 Beano Book. The bird and animal action drawings are amongst Paddy Brennan's best.

Go, Harrk!
The Bird Boy's foot lashed out just as the deckhand squeezed the trigger-
NO! You have plenty of whale meat on your ship. To shoot a young seal is needless and cruel!
But Kelvin's surge of anger had brought disaster. The shot had struck young crewman, Tim Richards in the head.
He's seriously injured. He must get to a hospital.
Although caused by that man's stupidity, this is my fault. Get the dog team.
The nearest hospital is at Harper's Bay. It shouldn't take me too long!
Kelvin made good progress until they reached the edge of the thawing ice-
The dog! Harrk! To me!
After him, Harrk! A Killer whale is closing in.

Harrk's wings tilted and the albatross sliced quickly towards the sled dog. Using his legs, Kelvin plucked the terrified dog from the jaws of the Antarctic's fiercest predator.
Excellent, Harrk!
Kelvin quickly hitched the dog to the team —
They set off as the biting Antarctic wind howled in its ferocity.
It's no good Harrk! The dogs are exhausted.

The Bird Boy dragged slabs of broken ice and fashioned them into a shelter for the injured man.
Now we sit out this storm!
The dogs huddled round in the shelter as the storm howled and battered for an hour before suddenly abating-
Oh, no! The ice has broken off and we're floating out to sea!

Harrk appeared from the crystal clear sky and glided low towards Kelvin-
Good, Harrk! Help me, seals. Guide us back towards the shore.
The seals nosed the ice floe back towards the shore-
We are almost there!
Once on solid ice, the Bird Boy hitched up the sled and hurried to Harper's Bay with fear in his heart as young Tim was deteriorating-
Harpers' Bay may be too far for us...hey, that's a naval vessel! Harrk, take me!
The frigate was an Australian vessel on patrol in the Antarctic. Harrk landed Kelvin on the bridge-
What the....?
I need help. A man is seriously injured. Do you have a surgeon or doctor.
Yes we do. Where is this man?
It took only a few minutes to transfer him to the frigate.
We can do an emergency operation to relieve the pressure...but it is risky!
Kelvin waited anxiously for over an hour before being told all was well. The huskies and sled were loaded onto the frigate to be returned to the whaler and The Bird Boy and Harrk wheeled away out over the icy, white wilderness.

Typical Dandy laughs from the 60's.

Drawn by the prolific comic strip artist George Martin.

An early Roger, drawn by Ken Reid.

Pet problems from the wildest boy in comics.

PETS' PICTURE GALLERY
MORE ANIMAL ANTICS
STOP HORSING AROUND AND PUSH THAT BUTTON!
I'M NOT FALLING FOR THAT OLD PULL MY FINGER TRICK!
NOW, THIS IS GOING TO BE SOME OMLETTE!
YOU'RE RIGHT, DOBBIN! HUMANS DON'T LOOK ANY BETTER THIS WAY!
I'M FEELING A LITTLE HUSKY! ANYBODY GOT A ZUBE?
IF I'M A LITTLE ELF, ARE YOU SANTA CLAUS?

STARTING TODAY!
GNASHER'S TALE
Many years ago, young Dennis, Pie-Face and Curly were collecting creepy-crawlies—
HI, PALS—WANT TO KNOW HOW DENNIS AND I MET?
COO! LOVELY CREEPIES!
SLOOP!
THEY TICKLE!
RUN! IT'S THOSE AWFUL MENACES!
YAH!
HERE'S CREEPY-CRAWLIES!
Later—
OOH! WHAT A SUPER HAIRY CATER-ER — CATER-ER — CRAWLY!
Back home—
HERE'S A NICE LETTUCE, LITTLE CRAWLY—HEY! THAT'S DAD'S DINNER!
CHOMP!
SLURP!
YOU—YOU THING! YOU'VE SCOFFED MY SAUSAGES!
PROD
BURP!
OOYAH! GET RID OF THIS BRUTE, DENNIS!
CRUNCH!
Soon—
GOOD! NO SIGN OF THAT HORRID CREEPY CRAWLY.
HEH! HEH! I'M NOT GIVING UP MY PET FOR ANYONE!
GNASH!
BNO. 21.5.77

You've read Gnasher's version of how he and Dennis met! Now read the real version!

Gnasher broke into the movies in 1978.

...AND THE FOLLOWING WEEK

THEN HE WAS LOST...

BUT AT LAST THE GALLANT "BRIGHT FANG" IS VICTORIOUS.

SLEDGE PULLING CONTEST

IN THE TOWNSHIP, THEY'RE HOLDING A CONTEST TO FIND THE STRONGEST SLED DOG

WITH ONE TWITCH OF HIS POWERFUL SHOULDERS, "BRIGHT FANG" SHIFTS THE HEAVY SLEDGE —

GOOD JOB HE"S ON FRIENDLY TERMS BRUCETHE MOOSE.

BUT HE WAS FOUND AGAIN...

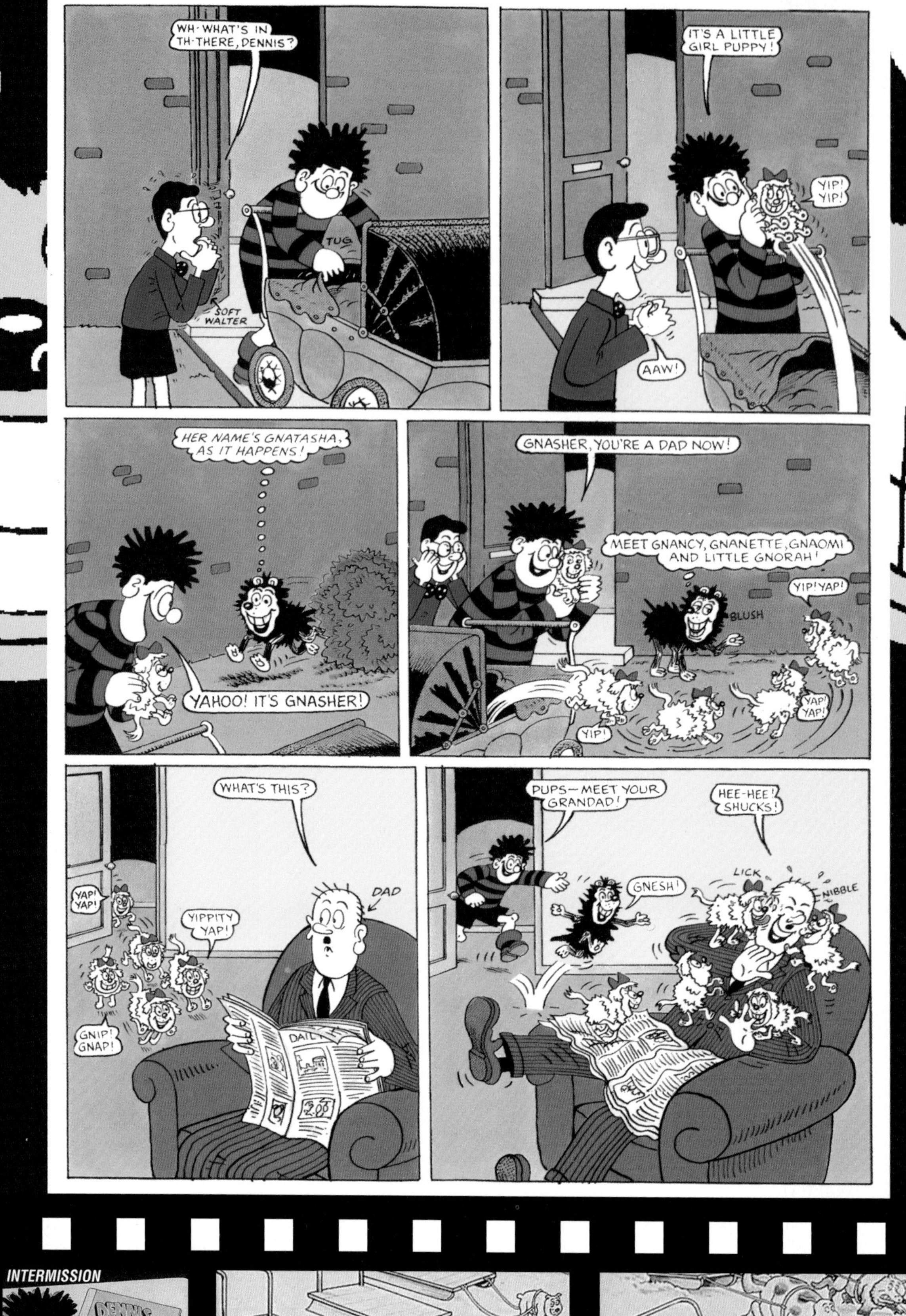

INTERMISSION

NEXT DAY THE TRAPPERS HAVE A "DOG DERBY" TO FIND THE FASTEST SLEDGE DOG IN THE NORTH—

"BRIGHT FANGS" MAYBE NOT THE FASTEST, BUT HE SURE IS THE CRAFTIEST.

...WITH SOME EXPLAINING TO DO!

INTRODUCING RASHER...

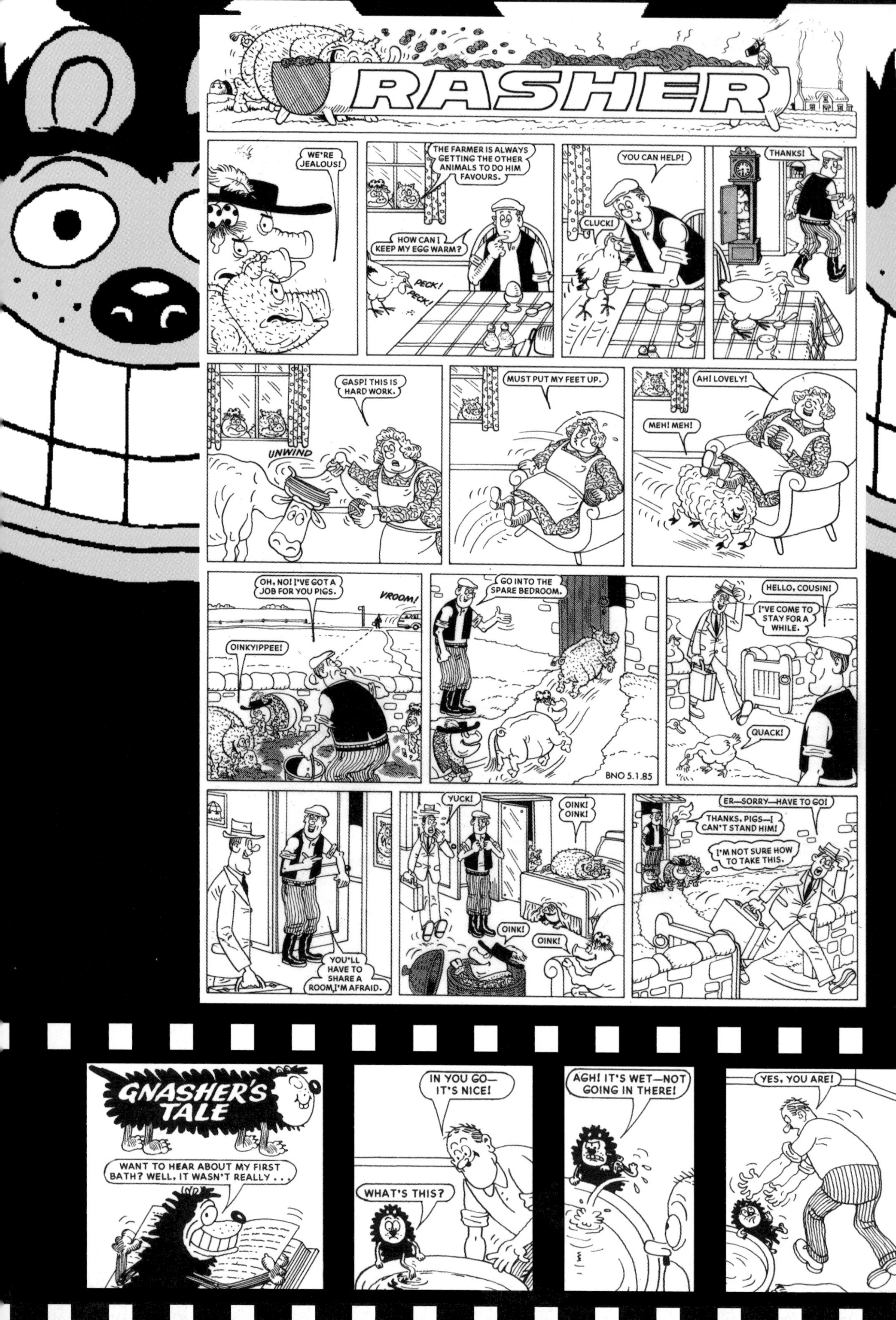

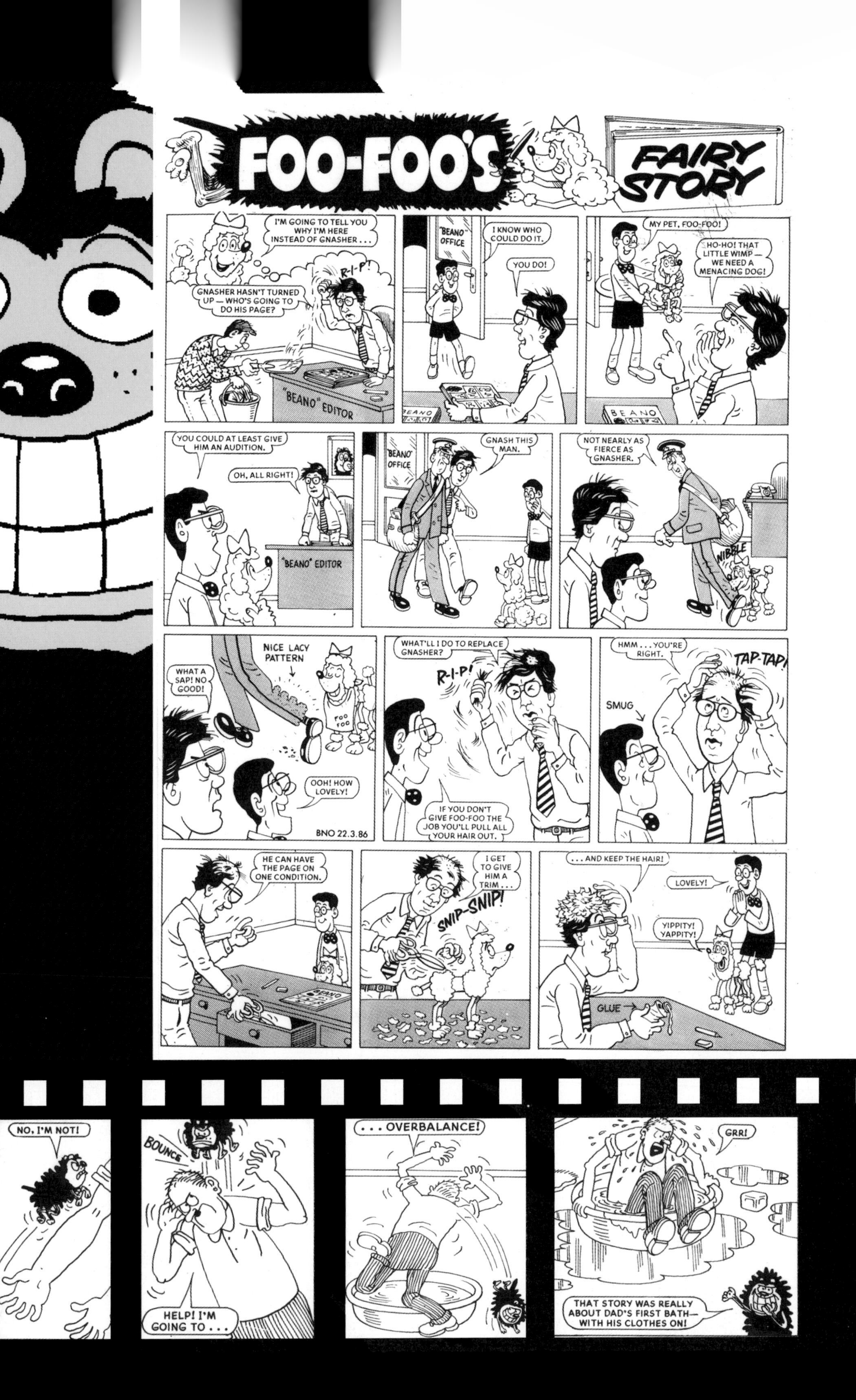
FOO-FOO'S
FAIRY STORY
I'M GOING TO TELL YOU WHY I'M HERE INSTEAD OF GNASHER . . .
GNASHER HASN'T TURNED UP — WHO'S GOING TO DO HIS PAGE?
R-I-P!
"BEANO" EDITOR
"BEANO" OFFICE
I KNOW WHO COULD DO IT.
YOU DO!
BEANO
MY PET, FOO-FOO!
HO-HO! THAT LITTLE WIMP — WE NEED A MENACING DOG!
BEANO
YOU COULD AT LEAST GIVE HIM AN AUDITION.
OH, ALL RIGHT!
"BEANO" EDITOR
"BEANO" OFFICE
GNASH THIS MAN.
NOT NEARLY AS FIERCE AS GNASHER.
NIBBLE
WHAT A SAP! NO GOOD!
NICE LACY PATTERN
FOO FOO
OOH! HOW LOVELY!
BNO 22.3.86
WHAT'LL I DO TO REPLACE GNASHER?
R-I-P!
IF YOU DON'T GIVE FOO-FOO THE JOB YOU'LL PULL ALL YOUR HAIR OUT.
HMM . . . YOU'RE RIGHT.
TAP-TAP!
SMUG
HE CAN HAVE THE PAGE ON ONE CONDITION.
BEANO
I GET TO GIVE HIM A TRIM . . .
SNIP-SNIP!
. . . AND KEEP THE HAIR!
LOVELY!
YIPPITY! YAPPITY!
GLUE
NO, I'M NOT!
BOUNCE
HELP! I'M GOING TO . . .
. . . OVERBALANCE!
GRR!
THAT STORY WAS REALLY ABOUT DAD'S FIRST BATH— WITH HIS CLOTHES ON!

DENNIS the MENACE and GNASHER
LASER QUEST
I WON THE LASER CHALLENGE, BUT I'M RUNNING LATE. MUST FIND MY DOG.
PURR!
WHINE! MY GNOSE!
THAT MENACING MUTT'S HAD A FIGHT TO PASS THE TIME.
At the vet's —
HERE, GNASHER. THIS'LL GNUMB YOUR GNOSE.
THE SHAME.
SCRATCHED SNOUT SALVE
MY SNIFFER BANDAGED. HOW WILL I SMELL?
AWFUL!
HMM. YOU HAVE TO BE CLEVER TO BE A VET, AND I'M CLEVER.
I'LL LEARN IT ALL IN ONE DAY. LET'S SEE — HICCUPING HIPPOS . . .
BE A VET IN SEVEN DAYS!
. . . WOOZY WOMBATS . . .
GROAN. LOOK AT THAT SOFTY STUDYING ALL THROUGH THE NIGHT.
Next morning —
I'VE LEARNED EVERYTHING. ALL I NEED IS A LITTLE PRACTICE. I'M NEARLY A VET!
HMM.
HI, MR ROAD ROLLERER. I'M A VET, YOU KNOW.
A BIT YOUNG, AREN'T YOU?
THANKS!
DID YOU HEAR THAT, GNASHER? A MINUTE AGO THE SOFT ITEM WAS NEARLY A VET AND NOW HE THINKS HE IS ONE!

PUP PARADE
with THE BASH STREET DOGS
See what my master let me borrow!
Gosh! A wooden turnip!
No, stupid—it's a spinning top!
You don't seem to be on TOP form today, Bones!
The trouble with Bones is he has no sense of humour!
Don't worry! I, Spinner the Spider, will help!
What's Spinner doing with his web?
YAHOO!
He's my pal, you know!
WHIZZ!
Spinner could spin absolutely anything!
HUM!
BUT SHORTLY—
There's something I'd like YOU to spin for me.
I don't believe it!
Kindly follow me.
Why is he going in here, I wonder?
PLAYPARK
This is what I want you to spin! It's too heavy for me!
WAHEY! THIS IS GREAT FUN!
SPIN-N-N

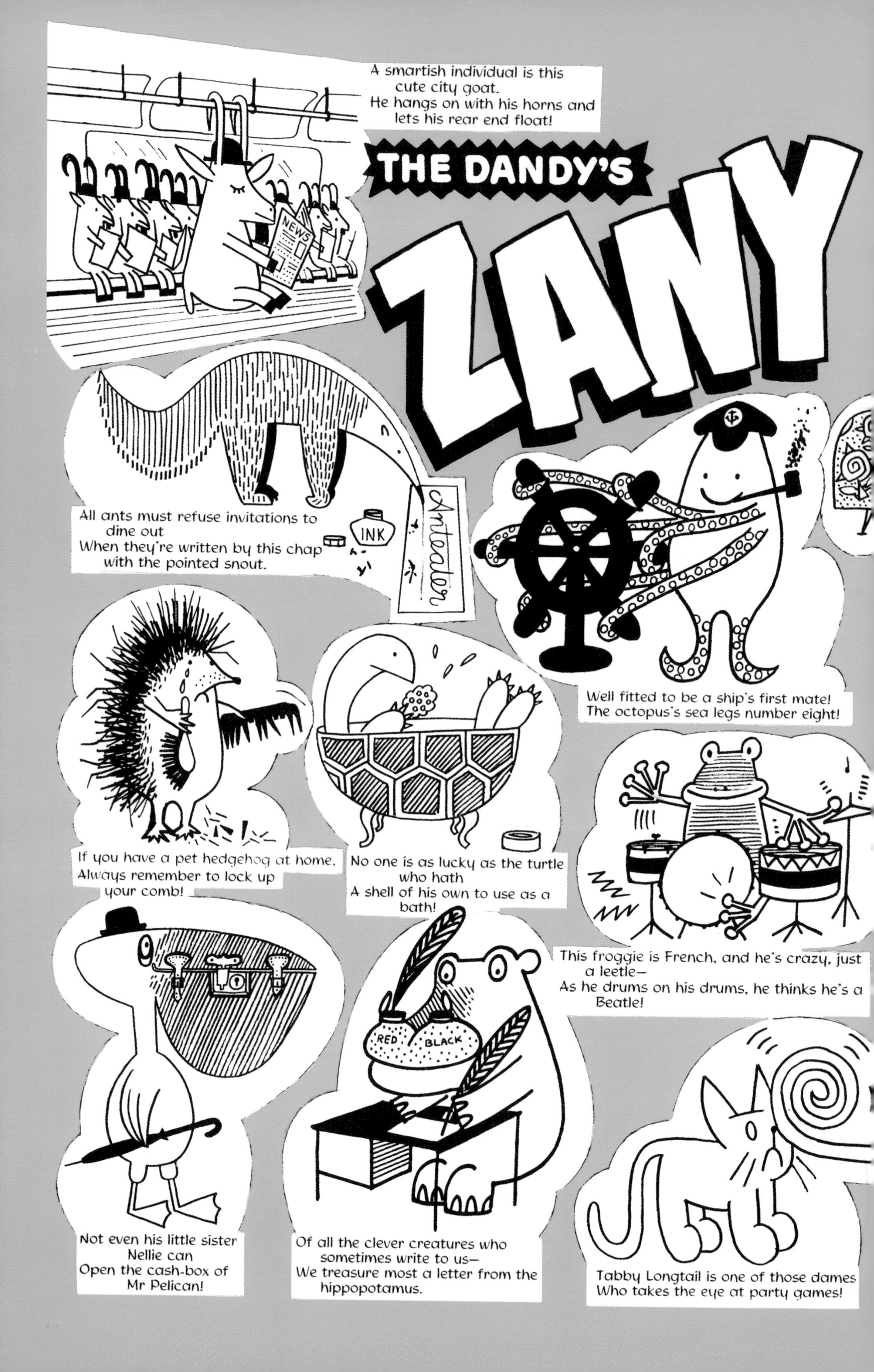
A smartish individual is this cute city goat.
He hangs on with his horns and lets his rear end float!
NEWS
THE DANDY'S
ZANY
All ants must refuse invitations to dine out
When they're written by this chap with the pointed snout.
INK
Anteater
Well fitted to be a ship's first mate!
The octopus's sea legs number eight!
If you have a pet hedgehog at home,
Always remember to lock up your comb!
No one is as lucky as the turtle who hath
A shell of his own to use as a bath!
This froggie is French, and he's crazy, just a leetle—
As he drums on his drums, he thinks he's a Beatle!
RED
BLACK
Not even his little sister Nellie can
Open the cash-box of Mr Pelican!
Of all the clever creatures who sometimes write to us—
We treasure most a letter from the hippopotamus.
Tabby Longtail is one of those dames
Who takes the eye at party games!

ZOO
TO THE ZOO
When the giraffe is driving, he draws gasps and glares,
For his seat is down below while his eyes are both upstairs!
Why is there a daytime smile on the face of the crocodile?
Because he keeps his teeth so white by always taking them out at night!
See the pains the walrus takes
Trying to pull a tusk that aches!
Baby Kangaroo is glad his mummy had the brains
To fix a little hood upon his shelter when it rains!
Hannah's a horse, but a laundry maid too—
She irons the dresses with a hot horse shoe!
A Merry Christmas and a Happy New Year—
That's the message from our bell-ringing deer.
MERRY XMAS
BED OF NAILS
The Indian Fakir hedgehog has the happy knack
Of carrying, when travelling, his bed upon his back!

Traditional Dandy SMASH! BANG! WALLOP! laughs.
the Jocks and the Geordies
ANGUS
HECTOR
SANDY
WEE ECK
BIG JOCK
SIDNEY
CEDRIC
EGBERT
ARNOLD
LANKY
IT'S GREAT BEING A GEORDIE!
BEIN' A GEORDIE MEANS YOU LIKE WHIPPET RACING—
— I LIKE RACING MY WHIPPET AGAINST THE JOCKS!
SHRIEK!
GEORDIES KEEP PIGEONS TOO!
MINE ARE CARRIER PIGEONS!
COO! COO!
BARK!
THEY'RE CARRYING ROTTEN EGGS!
UGH!
SPLAT!
SPLAT!
OOH!
DAN 18.4.87
JOCKS LIKE SWORD DANCING.

The comic was famous for its robust fun.

A Beano aristocrat from the 1974 book.

For Snooty, defeat—and a quick retreat!
THE GASWORKS GANG ARE CHALLENGING US TO A SNOWBALL FIGHT, SNOOTY!
RIGHT! WE'LL GET ANGUS TO LEAD US IN A CHARGE AGAINST THEM!
ANGUS THE BUNKERTON STAG
SHORTLY—
C-H-A-R-G-E—! PROD THEM WITH YOUR ANTLERS, ANGUS!
BUT—
BOUNCE
HAW! HAW! WE'RE NOT SCARED OF A STAG WITH BLUNT ANTLERS!
OOF!
AND—
TAKE THAT!

YOU'LL HAVE TO SHARPEN UP THOSE ANTLERS IF YOU'RE TO LEAD OUR CHARGES, ANGUS!
PLOTTING
THEN—
WE'LL SHARPEN THEM FOR YOU, ANGUS!
NOT WITH THAT GREAT NASTY GRINDSTONE, YOU WON'T!
DON'T WORRY, ANTLERS— I WON'T LET THEM TOUCH YOU!
BRR! IT'S COLD TODAY! JUST LOOK AT THOSE ICICLES!

Victory's quick with an icicle trick!

EVEN MORE ANIMAL ANTICS
GET YOUR OWN COPY!
PETS' PICTURE GALLERY
"SHAGGLES"— I. Paine, Blewbury, Berks.
"HERBURT"— Sally George, Wolverhampton, Staffs.
"JASON"— Anna Winstanley, Weymouth, Dorset.
"SIMON"— Roger Fryatt, Dungworth, Yorks.
"ISAAC"— Agit Yogasundram Marlborough, Wilts
"IPSY-WIPSY"— Sheena Mark, Ballymena, Co. Antrim.
"MINNIE"— Elaine Cappleman, Hull, Yorks.
"SMOKEY"— Karen Godfrey, Bexley, Kent.
SEND A PICTURE OF YOUR PET TO "PETS' PICTURE GALLERY" — YOU COULD WIN 50p!
BNO 28.7.73

Peter Potter's
OTTERS
This complete animal adventure is very typical of The Dandy Annual. Shy creatures, the otters just made this one rare appearence in the 1972 book. Using a more realistic style the artwork is by Korky the Cat cartoonist Charlie Grigg.
IT was great to be a gamekeeper's son! Peter Potter was permitted to fish as often as he liked on the River Torr. But as he was reeling in a fine trout one day, he got a shock when a sleek dark shape leapt out of the water and bit a chunk out of the fish before plopping back into the river. Peter gasped. The cheeky thief was an otter.

Amazed, Peter stared after the raider. But it was such a thrill to see an otter that he didn't mind about his ruined fish.
Now the otter was scrambling up the far bank, its prize still grasped in its mouth.
The boy was even more thrilled to see two young otter cubs run to meet their parent, squealing with delight at the promise of food.
Peter trudged off towards home, while the cubs tore at their helping of tasty trout.
On the way, Peter met Mr Craven, the estate owner, and he was furious when he noticed the state of Peter's catch and heard the story of how it happened.

Mr Craven rode to Dad Potter's cottage, and gave an angry order to his game-keeper. "Get rid of those otters! I don't want to have my fishing ruined!"
"Come on, Peter! Let me see where their holt is," Dad said.
That was the name for the otters' home, and Peter knew he must show his Dad, though he didn't feel happy about it.
On the way, they saw Trotter Parsons, along at Whitegate Farm, having trouble with a horse that seemed to be in pain. "He's got toothache," said Trotter. "I'll send for Selsey, the vet."
When the Potters got to the river, they were lucky enough to sneak up on the family of otters at play. The cubs were sliding over and over again down a muddy bank and plunging into the river, like boys having fun on a water chute.
Dad lifted his gun—and Peter lifted a stone!

Plunk! The stone splashed into the water as Dad was taking aim. In a scurrying, furry mass the otters vanished in a twinkling into their holt.
Dad was furious! He didn't like killing otters any more than Peter did, but orders were orders, and Peter had ruined his chance with that stone.
That night, Peter Potter left his bedroom by the window, taking a leather gauntlet that belonged to his Dad.
Climbing down to the otters' holt, Peter pulled on the leather glove. He was sorry he had ever mentioned the otters to Mr Craven, and so caused them to be hunted by his Dad, but now he could try to make amends.
Peter's plan was to grab hold of the otter cubs and take them away to a safe place, for the parents would be sure to desert their home and follow.
But the plan didn't work. "Ow!" He yanked his arm out. Deep slashes down his forearm streamed with blood above the leather gauntlet!

The sudden pain made Peter lose his grip on the tree, and next thing he knew he was in the river. Squealing angrily, the grown-up otters darted out after him.
But Peter's Dad, out on the hunt again, was on the other bank of the river. He couldn't see very clearly, but he could hear the squeals. He raised his gun.
"No, Dad!" yelled Peter, springing upright in the water and throwing up his hands as if to protect the otters.
His cry came too late to stop the finger that pulled the trigger, but Dad was so startled to hear his son's voice that he jerked his gun up.
Peter ducked as a hail of shot blasted into the bank well above his head.
"Come here, you young fool!" roared Dad. He held out his gun-butt and jerked the scared lad ashore.

Peter got a fearful ticking-off as he trudged homewards.
And at home, as Dad dressed his arm, Peter was told he was to be locked in his room till the otters were destroyed.
Peter was feeling miserable next morning, when suddenly he noticed a car pass by. It was the car of Mr Selsey, the vet, on its way to Trotter Parsons' horse.
WHITEGAT FARM
In no time at all, Peter was out of the window and on his way to Trotter's stables. There was the car in the yard.
Trotter was holding the pain-maddened animal while the vet gripped its nose and prepared to blow a knock-out pill down its throat. On a bench quite close to Peter was the box of pills—and it was open!
PILLS

The pill acted quickly, and while Mr Selsey set about dealing with the horse's bad tooth, Peter nabbed two pills!

In his Dad's garden shed, Peter ground the pills into powder. Then he sprinkled the powder inside a couple of fish.

Off he went again, vaulting the wall unseen, and heading for the holt. He took a rope along, and a stout sack.

Peter planted the baited fish close to the holt.

Then, hidden in a bush, he watched tensely. At length an otter snout poked out of the holt. Would his plan succeed before his Dad arrived with the gun?

It did! The otters pounced on the doped fish, with the two cubs fighting for the biggest share.

The first victim of the dope was one of the cubs. It lay down sleepily, then rolled over, breathing heavily.

Its mother sniffed at it. Then a sudden noise and the bang of a gun across the river alarmed the whole family.

It was Dad Potter who caused the racket. He trippe
over a rope that had been rigged across his path
Peter, and his gun went off as he fell.

When Dad arrived on the river bank, of course, there wasn't an otter in sight. The parents had dragged the sleeping cub with them into the safety of the holt.
Dad knew it was no good waiting. And as soon as he left, Peter got busy pulling out the doped otters.

It was a big load for Peter, that sackful of sleeping otters.

But manfully he bore it right to the door of the only man in the district who might help him.

The vet came to his door when Peter knocked, and was he astonished when the boy opened the sack and tumbled the otters out!
J.A. SELSEY
VETERINARY
SURGEON

Night after night, for a whole week, Dad Potter loyally stuck to his job. He watched with ready gun for just a glimpse of an otter. But nothing stirred, and at last he discovered the holt was deserted and the otters gone.

Only Peter Potter and the vet knew where the otters went – to a lonely lake miles away over the moor. Mr Selsey had taken them in his car, and they woke up from their sleep in a new playground, where human beings never came to bother them, where the fish were plentiful, and the long hot days were safe for them.

A very popular strip from the 80's.

We get many requests to show this strip again.

THE LAUGHING PLANET'S A-Z OF ANIMALS WITH DAVID CHATTENBOROUGH PART I
AS ONE OF THE LAUGHING PLANET'S FEATURES, WE PRESENT AN 'A' TO 'Z' OF CREATURES.
ENDING WITH ZEBRAS AND STARTING WITH ANTS. WITH MONKEYS AND RABBITS AND ELEPHANTS.
THE BUSIEST PLACE IN THE ANIMAL WORLD IS A NEST OF ANTS...
NOSEY POKE!
ANT HILL
HURRY! SCURRY! SCUTTLE! SCAMPER!
LOO
FLUSH!
THEY'RE BUSY WORKING ALL DAY LONG. THEY MUST HAVE ANTS IN THEIR PANTS.
OKAY, HE'S GONE.
TEABREAK, LADS!
CHAR
TEA
LOUNGE!
LAZE!
ROSY
IN AMERICA NOW, WE SAY 'HELLO', TO A PASSING BUFFALO!
HE'S NEVER BEEN THE SAME SINCE HE APPEARED IN 'DANCES WITH WOLVES'!
NO AUTOGRAPHS, DUDES.
VWAARM! VRRRAMM!
WITH FOUR LONG LEGS AND A LUMPY HIDE, THE CAMEL PROVIDES A BUMPY RIDE.
JIGGLY-JOGGLY-BIMPY-BUMP!
CHILLED DATE JUICE
WELL, WHAT D'YOU EXPECT? SHOCK ABSORBERS?
THE DOG IS KNOWN AS MAN'S BEST FRIEND. YOU CAN PLAY WITH HIM IN THE PARK. HE'LL STICK WITH YOU UNTIL THE END...
PAT! PAT!
...AND HIS BITE IS WORSE THAN HIS BARK.
NAUGHTY, FLUFFIES! LEAVE THAT BIG NOSED GENTLEMAN ALONE.
REMEDY FOR BEING NIPPED IN THE NETHERS
GNNASH! GNNAWW! GNIBBLE!
DAN 5.10.91
I'VE TRAVELLED ACROSS THE SEVEN SEAS, AND SEEN LOADS OF BEASTS, BY GUMBO.
RUSTLE!
MINCE AND MUSHROOM POULTICE.
BUT I'VE NEVER SEEN AN ELEPHANT WHO CAN JUMP OUT OF TREES...
WITH QUITE AS MUCH FORCE AS DEAR JUMBO.
LOOK OUT BELOW!! TOO LATE!
PHWEE-EEE! PLUMMET!
AAIEE!
SQUIMPH! SQUINGE! SQUODGE! SQUAAPHH!
SMALL AND GREEN AND STANDING ON A LOG, HOW I LOVE MY LITTLE PET FROG. YOUR BODY IS FAT AND YOUR LEGS ARE THIN...
BLUEBOTTLE BUTTIE.
RIVETS!
STINK!
BUT UNLIKE PEOPLE SAY I DON'T HAVE WARTY SKIN.
JOIN ME NEXT WEEK FOR A LAUGH, WHEN THE LETTER 'G' STANDS FOR GIRAFFE.
RIVETS! RIVETS!

THE LAUGHING PLANET'S A-Z OF ANIMALS WITH DAVID CHATTENBOROUGH PART II
I'M GLAD YOU COULD JOIN ME, ONE AND ALL, FOR ANOTHER LOOK AT ALL CREATURES GREAT AND SMALL.
TRUNDLE! SQUEAK!
OOH, ME FAVOURITE TELLY PROGRAMME.
LONG LEGS, LONG NECKS, THEY'RE A BARREL OF LAUGHS. THEY'RE THE LITTLE KNOWN SILLY-WALKING GIRAFFES.
'ERE! YOU'RE NOT JAMES HERRIOT!
RAAASSP! THRRAART!
HIGHLY ECCENTRIC SAUNTERINGS!
TOTALLY RIDICULOUS PERAMBULATIONS!
PRUNE-BRAINED PRANCINGS!
THAT BIG ANIMAL THAT'S RUNNING AWAY FROM US, IS ONE TERRIBLY SHY AND BASHFUL HIPPOPOTAMUS.
RHYTHMICAL RHYMING RUBBISH!
MUFFLED NAUGHTY WORD!
BASHFUL OINKINGS!
IF YOU'RE JAMES HERRIOT, LET'S SEE YOU STICK YOUR HAND UP A . . . GRMPH!
GREENER THAN UNRIPE BANANAS, THESE LITTLE LIZARDS ARE CALLED IGUANAS.
I SHALL WRITE TO THE B.B.C. ABOUT THIS!
THE JACKASS IS NO ORDINARY MULE, HE'LL CARRY YOUR LOAD DOWN THE TRACK. BUT THIS ONE'S MADE ME LOOK LIKE A FOOL . . .
SWEATY PURPLE STRAIN!
The BIDE-A-WEE TWILIGHT HOME FOR DECREPIT DONKEYS.
DITHER! DODDER!
'COS I'M CARRYING HIM ON MY BACK!
HAY FLAVOUR COLA
CRAWL! STAGGER! STRAIN!
SMALL AND FAT AND COVERED IN HAIR, WHEN YOU SHAVE A KOALA IT BECOMES A LITTLE *BEAR.*
STONE THE CROWS, COBBERS. THIS CRAZY POM HAS SHAVED ALL ME FUR OFF.
BZZZ!
KEV THE KOALA
AYRE'S ROCK.
AREN'T THEY CUTE, THESE BABY SHEEP? SEE THE LAMBS CURLED UP ASLEEP.
BAAH! I CAN'T HEAR THE FILM FOR HIS POETIC PRATTLINGS.
SILENCE OF THE LAMBS
PROPERTY OF SEAVIEW HOTEL
KINDLY DO NOT MENTION CURRY, CUTLETS, OR MINT SAUCE.
DAN 12.10.91
IF YOU LIKE YOUR MUSIC FAST AN' FUNKY, WHY NOT GIVE THIS A TRY?
DEAD CRUCIAL SOUNDS!
YO DAYSKI
PUMPH! PHUMPH!
SQUIRT!
RASP-BERRY
STREAMIN' WITH FUNK!
STRUTTIN' HIS FUNKY STUFF!
PUMPIN' UP THE JAM.
GET RIGHT ON DOWN WITH M.C. MONKEY. HE'S A REAL HIP, HAIRY GUY!
YO! PACE! CHECK IT OWT! KICK IT ONE TIME! GET WICKED! ETC.
M.C. FUNKY MONKEY
THAT'S HIM! HE LEFT ME IN A JUNGLE!
THAT'S FOR KIDNAPPIN' ME GRANNY, YOU ROTTEN OL' JAMES HERRIOT, YOU!
HIT HIM, STANLEY!
WHOP! THWOP! THWAP!
WE'RE DONE THIS WEEK, SO HIT THE ROAD, HE'LL START NEXT TIME WITH THE NATTERJACK TOAD!

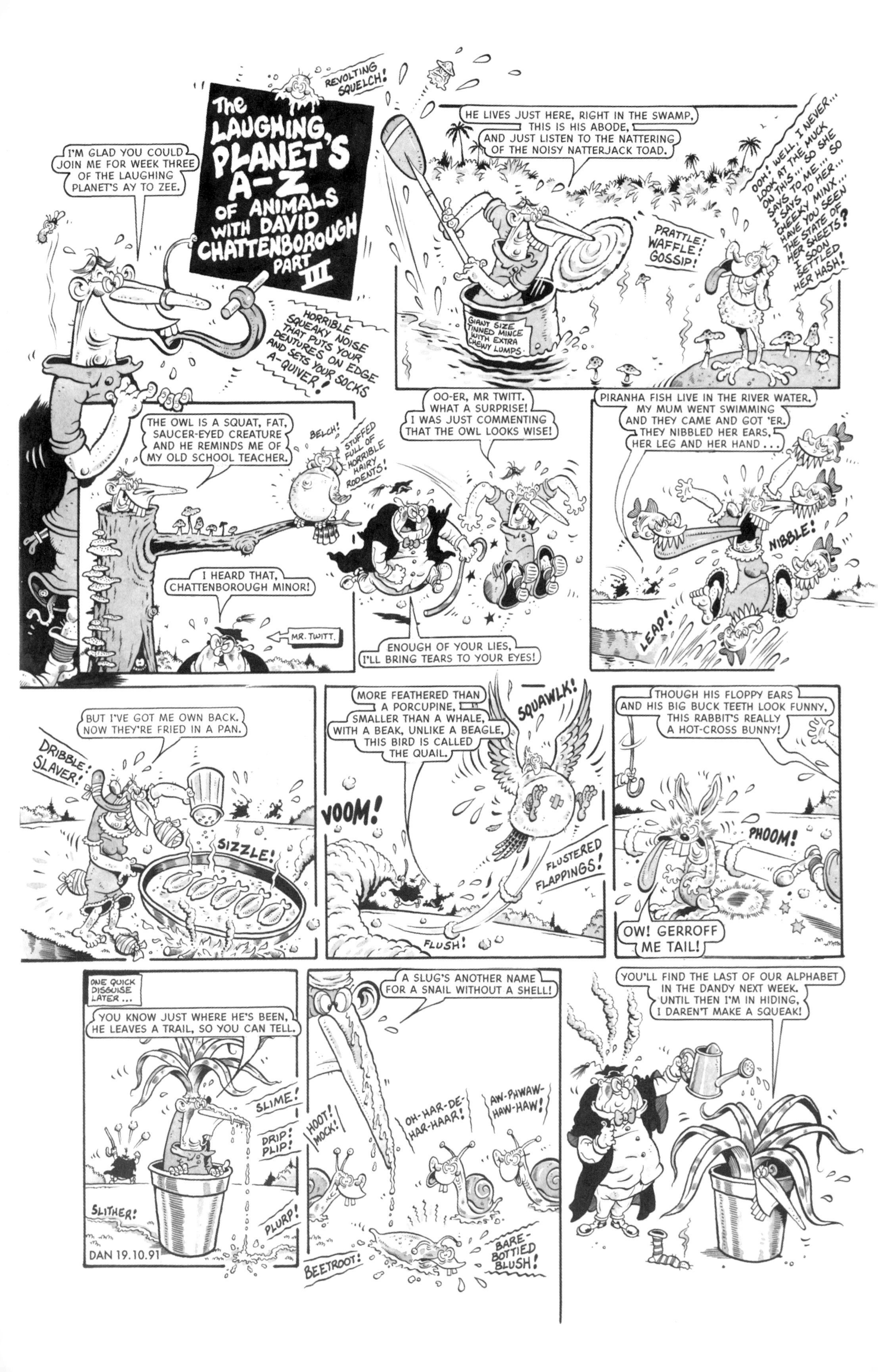
The LAUGHING PLANET'S A-Z OF ANIMALS WITH DAVID CHATTENBOROUGH PART III
I'M GLAD YOU COULD JOIN ME FOR WEEK THREE OF THE LAUGHING PLANET'S AY TO ZEE.
REVOLTING SQUELCH!
HORRIBLE SQUEAKY NOISE THAT PUTS YOUR DENTURES ON EDGE AND SETS YOUR SOCKS A-QUIVER!
HE LIVES JUST HERE, RIGHT IN THE SWAMP, THIS IS HIS ABODE, AND JUST LISTEN TO THE NATTERING OF THE NOISY NATTERJACK TOAD.
GIANT SIZE TINNED MINCE WITH EXTRA CHEWY LUMPS
PRATTLE! WAFFLE! GOSSIP!
OOH! WELL, I NEVER... LOOK AT THE MUCK ON THIS... SO SHE SAYS TO ME... SO I SAYS TO HER... CHEEKY MINX... HAVE YOU SEEN THE STATE OF HER SHEETS? I SOON SETTLED HER HASH!
THE OWL IS A SQUAT, FAT, SAUCER-EYED CREATURE AND HE REMINDS ME OF MY OLD SCHOOL TEACHER.
BELCH!
STUFFED FULL OF HORRIBLE HAIRY RODENTS!
I HEARD THAT, CHATTENBOROUGH MINOR!
MR. TWITT.
OO-ER, MR TWITT. WHAT A SURPRISE! I WAS JUST COMMENTING THAT THE OWL LOOKS WISE!
ENOUGH OF YOUR LIES, I'LL BRING TEARS TO YOUR EYES!
PIRANHA FISH LIVE IN THE RIVER WATER. MY MUM WENT SWIMMING AND THEY CAME AND GOT 'ER. THEY NIBBLED HER EARS, HER LEG AND HER HAND . . .
NIBBLE!
LEAP!
BUT I'VE GOT ME OWN BACK. NOW THEY'RE FRIED IN A PAN.
DRIBBLE! SLAVER!
SIZZLE!
MORE FEATHERED THAN A PORCUPINE, SMALLER THAN A WHALE, WITH A BEAK, UNLIKE A BEAGLE, THIS BIRD IS CALLED THE QUAIL.
SQUAWLK!
VOOM!
FLUSTERED FLAPPINGS!
FLUSH!
THOUGH HIS FLOPPY EARS AND HIS BIG BUCK TEETH LOOK FUNNY, THIS RABBIT'S REALLY A HOT-CROSS BUNNY!
PHOOM!
OW! GERROFF ME TAIL!
ONE QUICK DISGUISE LATER ...
YOU KNOW JUST WHERE HE'S BEEN, HE LEAVES A TRAIL, SO YOU CAN TELL.
SLIME!
DRIP! PLIP!
SLITHER!
PLURP!
DAN 19.10.91
A SLUG'S ANOTHER NAME FOR A SNAIL WITHOUT A SHELL!
HOOT! MOCK!
OH-HAR-DE-HAR-HAAR!
AW-PHWAW-HAW-HAW!
BEETROOT!
BARE-BOTTIED BLUSH!
YOU'LL FIND THE LAST OF OUR ALPHABET IN THE DANDY NEXT WEEK. UNTIL THEN I'M IN HIDING, I DAREN'T MAKE A SQUEAK!

BEFORE THIS ALPHABET BECOMES A BORE WE'LL FINISH IT OFF IN CHAPTER FOUR!
THE LAUGHING PLANET'S A-Z OF ANIMALS WITH DAVID CHATTENBOROUGH PART IV
THE TIGER IS AN ENORMOUS CAT, JUST LIKE A LEOPARD OR CHEETAH, BUT I'D BETTER RUN, THEY'RE NOT MUCH FUN . . .
EXPLORER STEW
SILENT FURTIVE SKULKINGS!
BELLAMY
DAINTY TIPPY-TOE!
. . . THIS STRIPEY MOG'S A MANEATER. YEEIKES!
JUMP!
ROOAAAAWRR!
WARBLE! CHIRRUP!
ALTHOUGH A MYTH, THE UNICORN, IS JUST A HORSE WITH A SINGLE HORN.
PAARPLE! BLAST! HONK!
SLAARP!
MYTHICAL BELCHINGS!
CUD FLAVOUR YOGHURT
UNMISTAKEABLE STENCH OF FEAR!
LIKE A FANG-FACED, FLYING RAT, IT'S THE BEASTLY BLOODSUCKING VAMPIRE BAT.
NIBBLE! SU-UCK!
FLIT! FLAP!
DROOBLE! SLOOB!
FRANTICALLY STUFFING GREAT DOLLOPS OF GARLIC PASTE DOWN HIS DRAWERS TO KEEP THE BLOODSUCKIN' BEASTIES AWAY.
GARLIC PASTE
GARLIC FLAVOUR ANTI-VAMPIRE SPRAY.
CASTLE DRACULA
THE WASP IS BLACK AND YELLOW, WITH A PAIR OF TINY WINGS. HE IS A BAD TEMPERED FELLOW . . .
BUZZ! ZZUZZZ!
I AM NOT, YOU SILLY, LONG-NOSED TWIT!
. . . AND IN HIS BOTTOM, HE HAS A STING! OUCH!
ONE OF BRUCIE'S OLD ONES.
PRAANG!
AGONISED UTTERANCES!
CHEAP POLYTHENE NOSH-MANGLERS BEING RATTLED TO FRAGMENTS.
SO DO YOU, BEAKY!
THE XYLOPHONE'S NOT AN ANIMAL REALLY, SO IT SHOULDN'T BE ON THIS LIST, IDEALLY.
XYLOPHONE MUSIC PLINKY-PLONKY-PLUNKITTY-PLUNK-KERPLUNKY PLONK!
THROBBIN' BOTTY!
CLOMP!
I'M STANDING IN THE FOOTPRINT, OF A CREATURE YOU'LL NEVER FORGET. HE'S OFTEN REFERRED TO AS BIG FOOT. BUT I'VE NOT SEEN A YETI YET!
DAN 26.10.91
ANOTHER STRIPEY ANIMAL, THOUGH NOT A TIGER, OF COURSE. SOME SAY THE NOBLE ZEBRA, IS A PYJAMA-WEARING HORSE.
ACTUALLY I AM A HORSE AND YOU'VE JUST WAKENED ME UP, CONK FACE.
WELL I'VE LISTED ALL THE ANIMALS DWELLING, FROM DELHI THROUGH TO DOVER, NOW WE CAN HEAVE A SIGH OF RELIEF. THIS ANIMAL ALPHABET'S OVER!
THE END!
CLIP! CLOP!

MINNIE the Minx
DAD HAS STRAINED HIS RIGHT ARM—
HEE! HEE! NO MORE WHACKS FOR ME FOR A LONG TIME!
I MUST DO SOMETHING ABOUT THIS!
TO KEEP YOU OUT OF TROUBLE UNTIL MY ARM'S BETTER I'VE ENROLLED YOU IN MISS FETLOCK'S RIDING CLASS.
OH, GOODY!
SHORTLY
AH, MINNIE! COME IN AND JOIN OUR LITTLE GROUP.
DELIGHTED, MISS!
FETLOCK'S STABLES
HORSES TO SUIT ALL SIZES
PLEASE DO NOT BITE THE HORSES

Minnie's steed is dusty indeed!

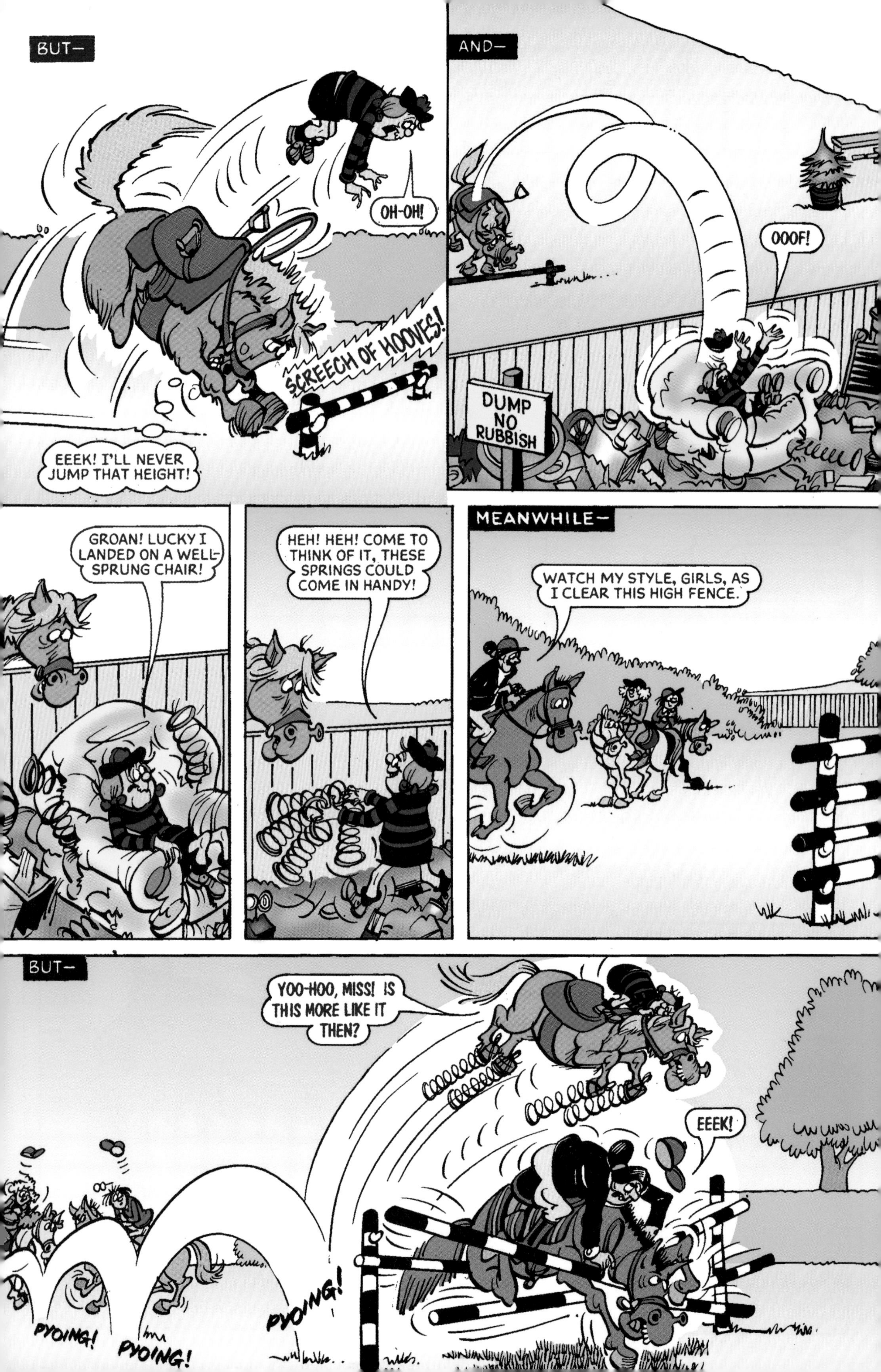

BUT–
OH-OH!
SCREECH OF HOOVES!
EEEK! I'LL NEVER JUMP THAT HEIGHT!
AND–
OOOF!
DUMP NO RUBBISH
GROAN! LUCKY I LANDED ON A WELL-SPRUNG CHAIR!
HEH! HEH! COME TO THINK OF IT, THESE SPRINGS COULD COME IN HANDY!
MEANWHILE–
WATCH MY STYLE, GIRLS, AS I CLEAR THIS HIGH FENCE.
BUT–
YOO-HOO, MISS! IS THIS MORE LIKE IT THEN?
EEEK!
PYOING!
PYOING!
PYOING!

A bouncing dash ends in a splash!

Dad has a spanking good horse!
AND MINUTES LATER—
GRR! MINNIE, I'VE BEEN HEARING ABOUT YOU!
B-BUT, DAD, YOU CAN'T WHACK ME—REMEMBER YOUR ARM!
HEAVE, GIRLS!
MAYBE I WON'T HAVE TO WHACK YOU!
MINX!
NOW BEND OVER, GIRL!
BUT, DAD—
AND—
WHACK!
EXCELLENT!
YEEEOW!
GROAN! WHAT A LIFE! DAD'S KEEPING THE HORSE UNTIL HIS ARM'S BETTER NOW!

Harry AND HIS HIPPO
THIS IS OUR "BE HELPFUL DAY". CAN I DO ANYTHING TO HELP YOU?
YES, YOU CAN GIVE MY HIPPO A WASH!
HUH! HE'S NOT GETTING ON VERY WELL AT ALL!
GOSH! THIS IS TIRING WORK.
SCRUB! SCRUB!
ZZZZZ
WASHING YOU HAS TIRED HIM OUT, HIPPO. LET'S GO AND BE HELPFUL IN HIS PLACE!
KEEP OUT
HELP! LET ME OUT!
Mc DUFFS WAREHOUSE
GOOD! HERE'S A CHANCE FOR US TO BE HELPFUL.
CRASH!
WELL DONE, HIPPO! THE MAN WHO SHOUTED WILL GET OUT NOW!
HEE-HEE! THANKS FOR HELPING ME ESCAPE!
BAH! YOU'VE LET SNEAKY SID GET AWAY!
LOOK AT THAT LITTLE GIRL CRYING, HIPPO. LET'S CHEER HER UP.
BOO-HOO!
HEE-HEE! HIPPO MAKE FUNNY FACE. HIPPO HAVE SWEETIE?
GLOOP!
I MEANT JUST ONE—AND YOU'RE WOLFING THE LOT!
GOBBLE!
I SAW THAT! TAKING MY LITTLE BESSIE'S SWEETS! COME BACK TILL I DEAL WITH YOU!
BOO-HOO-HOO! BAD HIPPO STEAL SWEETIES!
THAT MAN CAN'T GET ACROSS THE STREAM, HIPPO. LET'S HELP HIM.
THERE YOU ARE, SIR! YOU CAN CROSS OVER EASILY NOW.
BRRR!
OH, NO! TRUST HIPPO TO SNEEZE JUST THEN!
SPLUNGE!
ACHOO
SNARL! THIS IS "BE HELPFUL DAY" SO COME WITH ME!
GRAB!
DAN 5.1.80
I'M LEADER OF THE TROOP, AND I'VE NOW DONE THE MOST HELPFUL THING OF ALL!
POOR HIPPO! HE'S NEVER HELPFUL TO ANYONE BUT ME!

Monster mouse on the front cover.
THE Dandy 4d
EVERY TUESDAY. No. 1470—JAN. 24th, 1970.
KORKY the CAT
OUT! THE LOT OF YOU!
BOOT
WHAT A SHAME ON SUCH A FREEZING DAY!
WAIT TILL NIGHT. THEN WE'LL TEACH KORKY A LESSON.
THAT EVENING—
TAP-TAP
TAP-TAP
HELLO! SOMEBODY AT THE WINDOW!
WHO'S THERE?... EEK!
LET ME OUT OF HERE!
WHOOOSH
OH, G-G-GOSH!
HEE-HEE-HEE!
BACK INSIDE WE GO, BOYS!
BAH! DIDDLED!

Rat attack on the back.

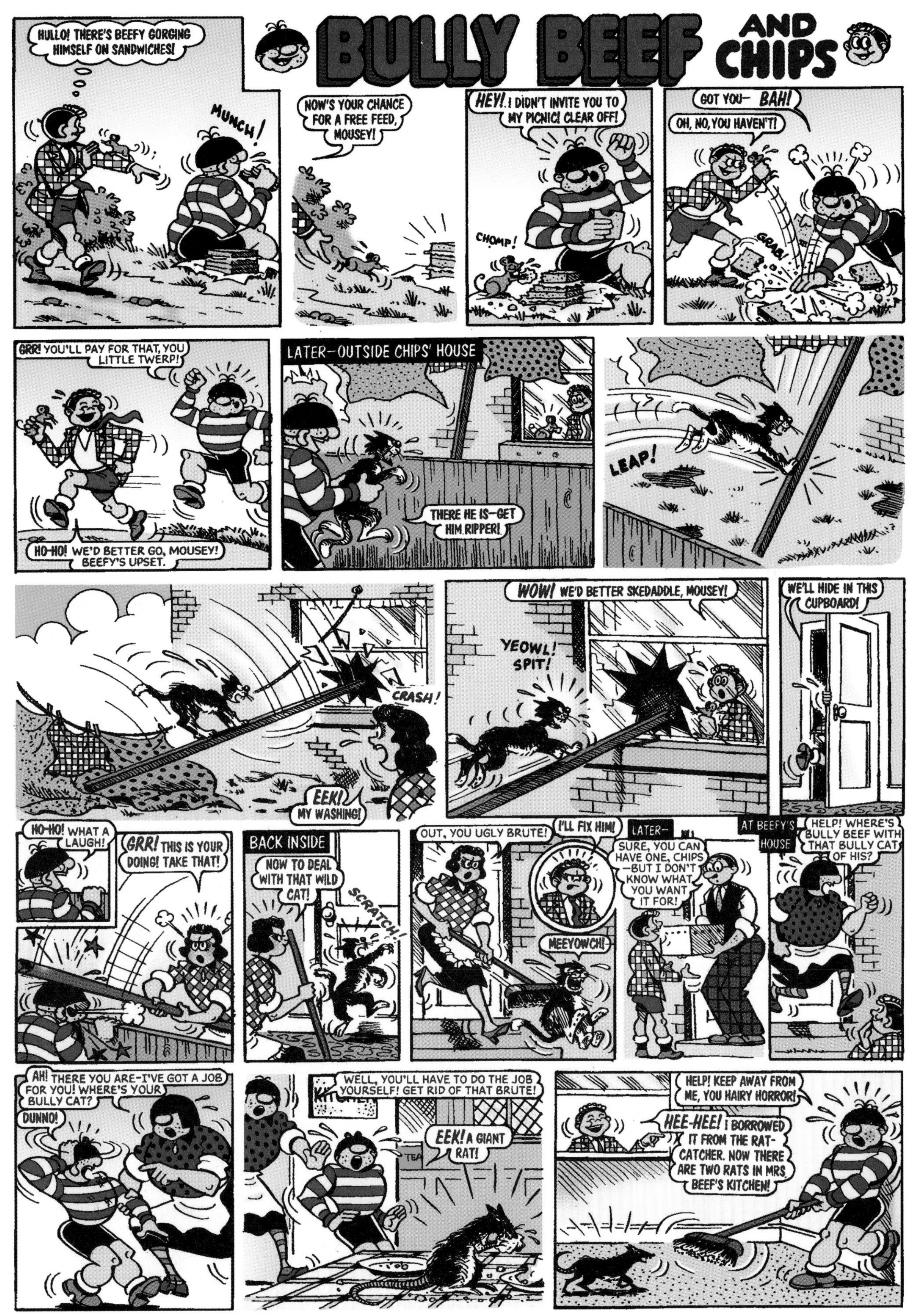

Some of the funniest animals that appeared in The Dandy and Beano were drawn by Ron Spencer. Ron started working for The Beano in 1962,taking over the Little Plum strip from Leo Baxendale. Here is a selection of his work that includes some brilliant creature cartooning.

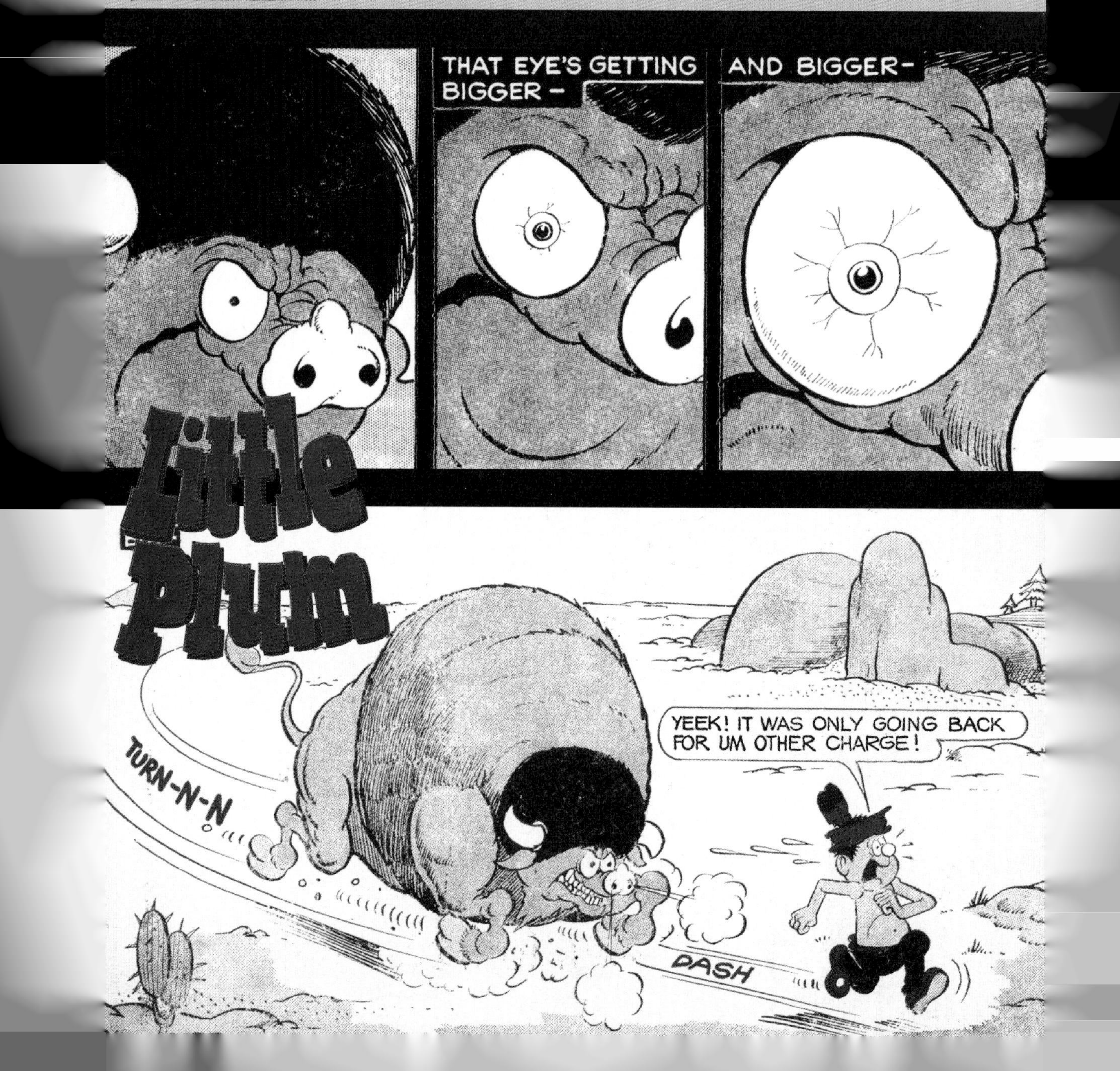

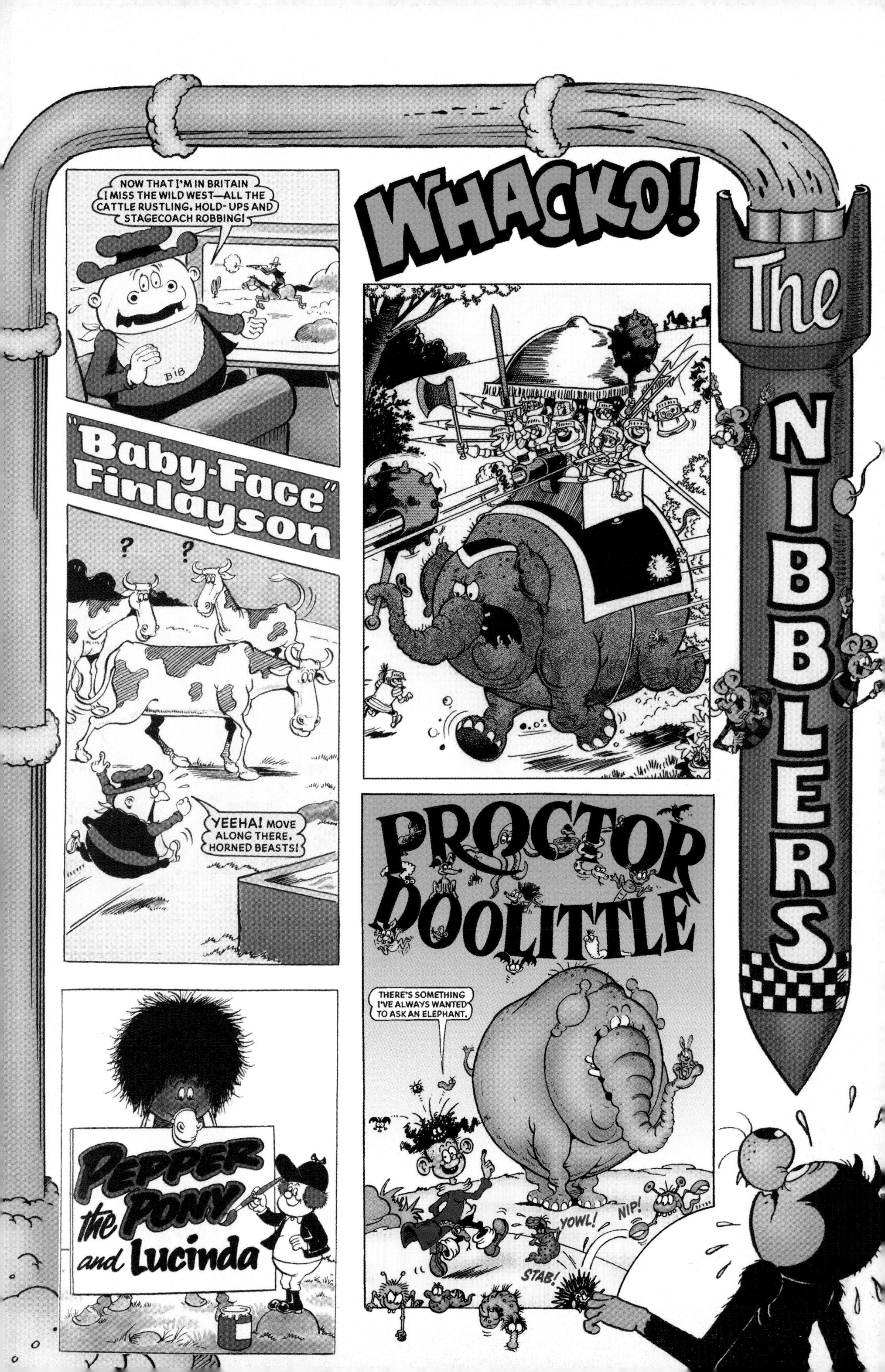
WHACKO!
The NIBBLERS
NOW THAT I'M IN BRITAIN I MISS THE WILD WEST—ALL THE CATTLE RUSTLING, HOLD-UPS AND STAGECOACH ROBBING!
BIB
"Baby-Face" Finlayson
?
?
YEEHA! MOVE ALONG THERE, HORNED BEASTS!
PROCTOR DOOLITTLE
THERE'S SOMETHING I'VE ALWAYS WANTED TO ASK AN ELEPHANT.
YOWL!
NIP!
STAB!
PEPPER the PONY and Lucinda

Gnasher does Becks.

But can he play footie without bursting the ball?

TWO STORIES ABOUT THE ZOO COMING NEXT.

BOTH STRIPS WERE ILLUSTRATED BY BARRIE APPLEBY.

STORYLINES WERE INSPIRED BY THE DANDY ED'S OWN CHILDREN.

THEY MUST HAVE BEEN PROPER LITTLE MONKEYS!

ROBBIE REBEL
NOBODY TELLS HIM WHAT TO DO!
DON'T YOU BE GETTING TOO COMFY ON THAT SOFA, ROBBIE.
ZZZ!
'COS IT'S YOUR BATH NIGHT!?!
IN YOUR DREAMS, DAD!
RIGHT! IF ROBBIE WON'T COME FOR HIS BATH . . .
. . . THE BATH WILL GO TO ROBBIE!
HE'S PUT WHEELS ON AN OLD TIN BATH. THE MAN'S MAD!
SCOOSH!
HEH! I GOT CLEAN AWAY. NOW I CAN PLAY DIRTY ALL DAY.
OINK
Soon —
DO NOT TEAR ALONG THE DOTTED LINE. BY ORDER.
Y'WOT?
ROBBIE REBEL TEARS ALONG DOTTED LINES IF HE WANTS.
HA-HAR! HE FELL FOR MY NOTICE!
TRIP!
GROOGH!
OH, NO! STOP!
I'VE HEARD OF RUNNING A BATH BUT THIS IS RIDICULOUS.
'ELLO, 'ELLO! YOU IS COMIN' WITH ME, LAD!
POLICE
OO-ER! I COULD BE IN HOT WATER.
HURTLE!
LOOK, I'LL COME CLEAN! THIS WAS MY DAD'S FAULT.
THAT EXCUSE WON'T HOLD WATER WITH THE JUDGE, ROBBIE.

However —
ZOO
ROAR!
I GOT YOUR CALL, WHAT'S THE PROBLEM?
NOW WHAT?
AAH! YOU'VE GOT ROBBIE REBEL. BRING HIM IN!
POLICE
SPLAT!
SPLASH!
SCOOT!
CHORTLE! WASH BEHIND THE EARS, YOU PAIR!
TUSKER'S ALWAYS IN A FOUL MOOD ON BATH NIGHT AND ONLY ROBBIE CAN HANDLE HIM.
WAHEY! TAKE THAT, TUSKER!
POLICE
KEN.H. HARRISON.
MARVO
The WONDER CHICKEN
with HENRY THRAPPLEWHACKER THE 49th.
CRUMP!
CRASH!
CRUNCH!
GNIPH!
TA-DA!

BONUS FEATURES

Recently unearthed in our archive a Desperate Dawg page. Scripted,drawn and lettered in pencil but never used. It would have been drawn around 1974 by George Martin.

THE THREE BEARS -
PA BEAR
MA BEAR
AND LITTLE
TEDDY BEAR
OINK! OINK!
IT'S...
NOSEY
PORKER
HE'S ALWAYS GOT HIS SNOUT
IN OTHER PEOPLES' BUSINESS!!
HI, AUNTIE ESTHER!

Early sketches by Leo Baxendale of the bear family who eventually became the famous Beano THREE BEARS strip.

The first ink of Desperate Dawg who ran in The Dandy 1973 – 1984. Drawn by George Martin.

Nosey Porker was a proposed strip for The Dandy. Tom Paterson did the drawings for this humanised piglet. Unfortunately,this little piggy didn't go to market and it stayed at home in the editor's file.

A card done for Esther Rantzen and her THAT'S LIFE tv team. Gnasher was penned by David Sutherland,the then current Dennis and Gnasher artist.

 Printed and published by D.C. Thomson & Co., Ltd., 185 Fleet Street, London EC4A 2HS. ISBN 978 1 84535 317 9

THE HILARIOUS BEARS INTRODUCED AND